The

Complete Guide

to the

CQE

◆◆◆

Solutions Manual

Thomas Pyzdek

Quality Publishing
Tucson, Arizona

Quality Publishing, Inc.
2405 N Avenida Sorgo, Tucson, Arizona 85749-9305
1-800-628-0432

Published 1996
Printed in the United States of America

04 03 02 01 00 99 98 97 96   5 4 3 2 1

ISBN 0-930011-30-9

♦ ♦ ♦

Contents

♦ ♦ ♦

Introduction

The goal of *The Complete Guide to the CQE* is to provide the materials you need to master the body of knowledge of quality engineering. Coincidentally, if you accomplish this you will also be able to pass the ASQC CQE exam. It is important to keep in mind that becoming certified is totally dependent on mastering the body of knowledge. The sole strategy of "studying the exam" by using books and primers focused on the exam itself is one big reason that 50% to 70% of those who sit for the CQE exam fail to become certified.

The Complete Guide to the CQE takes an entirely different approach. Although the exam isn't ignored completely, this program of study focuses on the body of knowledge, and this *Solutions Manual* is designed accordingly. There are four sections for each chapter in *The Complete Guide to the CQE*. The sections are listed here in order of importance to your learning the body of knowledge:

1. **Solutions to selected exercises**—Most (but not all) exercises that don't require you to draw upon your own experiences are solved in detail.

2. **Detailed solutions to selected past exam questions**—The CQE body of knowledge has changed very little over the years, and most of the changes involve reducing the scope of the body of knowledge. Thus, if you are planning to take the ASQC CQE exam, you will likely find

it worthwhile to practice with some questions that appeared in past exams. This section of the *Solutions Manual* lists several questions that relate to the material you read in *The Complete Guide to the CQE,* along with the correct answers, a detailed discussion of how to arrive at the answers, and a discussion of why some of the "close" choices were not correct.

3. **Simulated exam questions**—A few additional subject areas were added to the body of knowledge when it was last revised. Since ASQC no longer publishes exam contents, there is no way to know the precise wording of questions that cover the new material. However, it is possible to speculate. For new material you will find a section in the *Solutions Manual* entitled "Simulated Exam Questions." Detailed solutions are provided for these simulated questions.

4. **Other past exam questions**—Finally, all remaining ASQC CQE exam questions released by ASQC are listed in a section entitled "Other Past Exam Questions," along with their answers. These answers are not explained in detail, but if you have worked through the previous three sections you should have no trouble coming up with the correct answer.

Overall, the CQE body of knowledge has been narrowing in scope over the years. For example, mechanical inspection and product liability are no longer part of the body of knowledge. Only those past exam questions covered by the current body of knowledge are covered in this *Solutions Manual.*

The following approach is recommended:
1. Read *The Complete Guide to the CQE* carefully and completely. The recommended lesson schedule is described in the introduction to *The Complete Guide to the CQE.*

2. Attempt to answer the exercises covering the reading material without looking at the solutions in this book. If you have difficulty, review the reading material until you are able to complete the exercise, at least tentatively. Take one exercise at a time.

3. Look up the answer in this *Solutions Manual.* If you did the exercise incorrectly, correct your response and review the material in *The Complete Guide to the CQE. This repetition is a very important part of the learning process.*

4. The above three steps are sufficient for those whose interest is in learning the CQE body of knowledge. Those planning to take the ASQC CQE exam may wish to practice answering questions about the body of knowledge. After completing the exercises, attempt to answer the questions in the "Detailed solutions to past exam questions" section. We suggest that you first read the question without looking at the answer and try to answer the question. Then check to see if your answer is correct. Research shows that this "try first" approach improves retention.

5. Those planning to take the ASQC CQE exam should also look at the simulated exam questions covering new material.

6. Finally, those aspiring CQE's who want even more practice can get it by answering the other past CQE questions.

Quality engineering covers an extremely broad range of subjects. Mastering it is a difficult challenge that requires intense study. However, quality engineers are constantly in demand and they play a vital role in the success of their organization. It's a career rich in both monetary and non-monetary rewards. This program of study, rigorously followed, will help prepare you to share in the exciting opportunities that exist for qualified quality engineers.

I

General Knowledge, Conduct, and Ethics

A. SOLUTIONS TO SELECTED EXERCISES FOUND IN *THE COMPLETE GUIDE TO THE CQE*

1. *Name three key benefits that accrue to firms with a competitive advantage in quality.*

   Increased market share, higher profitability, greater return on investment, stronger customer loyalty, more repeat purchases, less vulnerability to price wars, lower marketing costs, lower costs, premium prices, higher rate of growth.

   (see section I.A.1 Benefits of quality)

2. *Write a memorandum to the plant manager describing quality systems standards and outlining the major benefits of adopting such a standard in her plant.*

   The memorandum should define what a quality systems standard is and list one or more of the purposes of standards (e.g., standards educate, simplify, conserve resources, provide a base on which to certify).

   (see section I.A.2 Domestic and international quality standards)

3. *Describe the ISO 9000 series and name at least two reasons for its popularity.*

The description should include a discussion of ISO 9000 as a hierarchy of standards and explain when each standard in the series is used. Two reasons for its popularity is that it reduces the need for second-party audits and provides a reasonably complete description of a quality system.

(see section I.A.2 Domestic and international quality standards)

4. *Describe the certification process under ISO 9000 and discuss the advantages and disadvantages compared to traditional second party audits.*

The certification process is described in the text. Advantages: ISO 9000 reduces the number of repetitive second-party audits, it provides consistent requirements, it is recognized by firms and governments around the world. Disadvantages: it can create a focus on becoming certified instead of achieving world-class quality, certification is costly and time-consuming, it does not incorporate customer-specific requirements.

(see section I.A.2 Domestic and international quality standards)

5. *Critique the following statement: "It is possible to be certified to ISO 9000 and yet to provide unacceptable quality."*

The statement is true. ISO 9000 merely requires that a quality system be developed and implemented. It is entirely possible that the system is not effective in providing quality that meets the requirements of a particular customer.

(see section I.A.2 Domestic and international quality standards)

6. *Describe at least two standards other than ISO 9000.*

The section entitled "other quality standards" describes several standards other than ISO 9000.

(see section I.A.2 Domestic and international quality standards)

7. *Describe the four eras of quality.*

The inspection era, the quality control era, the quality assurance era and the strategic quality management era should be listed and discussed.
(see section I.A.3 Quality philosophies)

8. *Shewhart used a process-focused approach to quality. Describe this approach and contrast it with the approach used prior to Shewhart.*

A process-focus attempts to identify key quality drivers and then to control the variation in these drivers. Prior to Shewhart quality was more or less defined as after-the-fact product inspection.
(see section I.A.3 Quality philosophies)

9. *What is the fundamental premise of quality assurance and how does it differ from quality control?*

Quality assurance is based on the premise that defects can be prevented and that there is an economically "optimum" quality level that balances prevention, appraisal and failure costs. Quality assurance views quality as a management concern and looks to the quality department for guidance in achieving quality. Quality control approaches quality as a technical problem with inspection and engineering components. Quality control focuses on controlling process variability.
(see section I.A.3 Quality philosophies)

10. *Compare strategic quality management with quality assurance.*

Strategic quality management views quality as both the lack of negatives (e.g., defects) and the presence of desirable features that customers notice. Strategic quality management looks outside of the firm for the final quality judgment, i.e., to the customer. Quality is seen as a means of achieving the firm's strategic goals. Due to its strategic importance, quality is seen as a board-level concern of the organization. Quality assurance, in contrast, defines quality using internal standards, e.g., engineering specifications. Quality is achieved when "zero defects"

are produced. Quality is largely the concern of the quality department, which coordinates the quality efforts of other departments and serves as a "policeman" through inspection and audit activities.
(see section I.A.3 Quality philosophies)

11. ***Pick any two of Deming's Fourteen points and explain a) their application to a real-world situation you've experienced, b) their relationship to each other.***
(see section I.A.3 Quality philosophies)

12. ***Provide at least one example of where a locally optimal solution leads to an undesirable global effect.***

There are limitless possibilities, e.g.: A purchasing department buys from the lowest bidder, leading to higher costs for manufacturing and the customer. Manufacturing cuts scrap and rework by relaxing their standards, leading to higher costs for the customer. Engineering meets their unrealistic deadline by releasing designs that cannot be produced, increasing manufacturing costs.
(see section I.A.3 Quality philosophies)

13. ***Describe the Baldrige criteria.***

The student should present a verbal description of the Baldrige criteria as a system for attaining world-class quality levels.
(see section I.A.3 Quality philosophies)

14. ***What is the fundamental principle of modern strategic quality management?***

"The customer is king!"
(see section I.A.3 Quality philosophies)

15. Name the five approaches to defining quality.

Transcendent, product-based, user-based, manufacturing-based and value-based.

(see section I.A.3 Quality philosophies)

16. What are the five criteria to consider when communicating?

The information must be timely, clear, accurate, relevant and believable.

(see section I.A.4 Communication and presentation skills)

17. Prepare an agenda for a meeting of yourself and a few classmates. The purpose of the meeting is to discuss the formation of a **Complete Guide to the CQE** *study group.*

(see section I.A.4 Communication and presentation skills)

18. Prepare a 3 minute speech on any topic covered in chapter I.

(see section I.A.4 Communication and presentation skills)

19. List the six principles of graphical integrity.

See text.

(see section I.A.4 Communication and presentation skills)

20. Bring in an example of a graphic which lacks graphical integrity.

On any given day one can find several such "gee whiz" graphics in almost any newspaper or magazine. *USA Today* is normally a good source.

(see section I.A.4 Communication and presentation skills)

21. Locate an engineering drawing used in your work and identify the different views.

See Figure I.7 in *The Complete Guide to the CQE.*

(see section I.A.5 Interpretations of diagrams, schematics, drawings, ...)

22. *Sketch the following lines: visible, hidden, long break.*
    See Figures I.9, I.10 and I.15 in *The Complete Guide to the CQE.*
    (see section I.A.5 Interpretations of diagrams, schematics, drawings, ...)

23. *One drawing specifies hole locations using geometric dimensioning and tolerancing (e.g., true position), another uses coordinate tolerancing (e.g., plus or minus), describe the shapes of the tolerance zones obtained using each method.*
    Geometric dimensioning will produce round tolerance zones, coordinate tolerancing produces square or rectangular tolerance zones.
    (see section I.A.5 Interpretations of diagrams, schematics, drawings, ...)

24. *Describe how a Gantt chart is used in project management.*
    Gantt charts are used to show the activities involved, their expected start and end dates, and to monitor the status of the project.
    (see section I.A.6 Project management skills)

25. *Select two or more project management tools and describe their use.*
    The student can choose from the following list: Gantt charts, Pareto diagrams, process decision program charts, QFD, matrix charts, arrow diagrams, or PERT networks.
    (see section I.A.6 Project management skills)

26. *You wish to prepare breakfast consisting of eggs, bacon, buttered toast and juice. Prepare a project plan.*
    Depending on the instructor's wishes, this can be either simple or elaborate. In simple form, the student might prepare a Gantt chart of the major activities. A more elaborate plan might employ several other tools.
    (see section I.A.6 Project management skills)

27. *Your phone rings just as you are leaving the office. The caller informs you that he is a small businessman and that your company's purchasing department is refusing to pay for the items he shipped to your firm because of a minor quality problem. If he doesn't receive payment soon, he will be forced to lay off several people. As the quality manager, the decision is yours. Discuss the ethical implications of this situation.*
(see section I.A Professional conduct and ethics)

B. DETAILED SOLUTIONS TO SELECTED PAST EXAM QUESTIONS

1. *Products should be subjected to tests which are designed to:*
    a. demonstrate advertised performance.
    b. demonstrate basic function at minimum testing cost.
    c. approximate the conditions to be experienced in customer's application.
    d. assure that specifications are met under laboratory conditions.
    e. assure performance under severe environmental conditions.

    Under the "fitness for use" definition of quality, choice *c* is the best. Keep in mind that if a different context were presented one of the other choices might be better (e.g. choice *e* might be best for a prototype guided missile).

2. *In the drawing tolerance* | $\oplus$ | 0.005 | $\circledM$ | A | B | C |, *C is the:*
    a. primary datum.
    b. tertiary datum.
    c. basic datum.
    d. largest datum.

    ANSI Y14.5M-1982 Section 4.3 states:
    "To properly position a part on the datum reference frame, datums must be specified in an order of preference."

The datum reference frame described involves three mutually per-pendicular datum planes. Datum features which are to be used to establish these datum planes are shown in the feature control block in order of precedence, as shown below

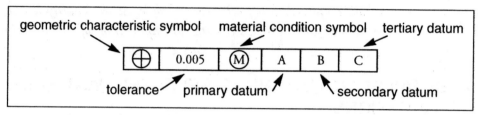

Thus choice *b* is correct.

(see page 46)

3. *In life cycle costing, the term "life" refers to whose viewpoint?*
   a. producer's.
   b. user's.
   c. contractor's.
   d. quality control.

   Life cycle cost concepts are based on the user's perspective; choice *b* is best. Life cycle cost takes into account purchase price, maintenance costs, resale value, etc.

4. *A successful quality circle program should produce all of the following benefits except:*
   a. improved worker morale.
   b. decreased need for management efforts to maintain quality.
   c. improved communication between managers and quality circle members.
   d. cost savings from participative problem solving.

   No quality program decreases the need for management efforts to maintain quality. Choice *b* is correct.

5. *Historic levels of defects, with rare exceptions, have been found to be located at what point, with respect to the optimum point in the figure?*

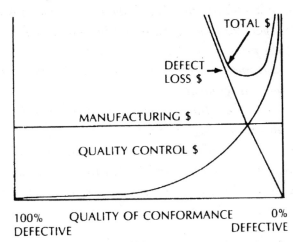

a. *to the left of the optimum.*
b. *to the right of the optimum.*
c. *at the center of the optimum.*
d. *none of the above.*

Historically, the defect rate has been higher than optimum, or to the left of optimum on the graph shown. Choice *a* is correct. The reasons that this has been are so many and varied as to be worth a book all their own (in fact, such best sellers as *In Search of Excellence, Theory Z,* and *Japanese Manufacturing Techniques* address this problem); a brief discussion is provided in the articles by Harrington cited above.

6. *In consumer products, the complaint rate is most directly a measure of:*
a. *product quality.*
b. *customer satisfaction.*
c. *market value.*
d. *rejection rate.*
e. *specification conformance.*

The key words are "most directly." Choice *b* is most directly measured by the customer complaint rate.

7. *In spite of the Quality Engineer's best efforts, situations may develop in which his decision is overruled. The most appropriate action would be to:*

    a. *resign his position based upon his convictions.*

    b. *report his findings to an outside source such as a regulatory agency or the press.*

    c. *document his findings, report to his superiors, and move on to the next assignment.*

    d. *discuss his findings with his co-workers in order to gain support, thereby forcing action.*

The "correct" answer to this question depends on the circumstances. In matters of safety and health threats you are at times morally and legally obligated to take the actions described by choices *a* or *b*. However, in the vast majority of cases choice *c* is best.

C. SIMULATED EXAM QUESTIONS

1. *ISO 9000 is:*

    a. *a catalyst used in petroleum refining.*

    b. *an international standard for acceptance sampling by attributes.*

    c. *the name commonly used to describe a series of international standards and guidelines for quality systems.*

    d. *the international equivalent to the Malcolm Baldrige National Quality Award.*

ISO 9000 is a set of five standards for quality systems, choice *c*. The titles are shown in the table below.

STANDARD	TITLE
ISO 9000-1	Part 1: Guidelines for selection and use
-2	Part 2: Generic guidelines for application of ISO 9001, 9002 and 9003
-3	Part 3: Guidelines for application of ISO 9001 to development, supply and maintenance of software
-4	Part 4: Application for dependability management

Continued on next page . . .

Continued from previous page . . .

STANDARD	TITLE
ISO 9001	Quality Systems—Model for Quality Assurance in Production, Installation, and Servicing
ISO 9002	Quality Systems—Quality Assurance in Production, Installation, and Servicing
ISO 9003	Quality Systems—Model for Quality Assurance in Final Inspection and Test
ISO 9004-1	Part 1: Guidelines
-2	Part 2: Guidelines for services
-3	Part 3: Guidelines for processed materials
-4	Part 4: Guidelines for quality improvement
-5	Part 5: Guidelines for quality plans
-6	Part 6: Guidelines for project management
-7	Part 7: Guidelines for configuration management
-8	Part 8: Guidelines on quality principles

The guidelines in ISO 9000 are being adopted worldwide and they are being used to certify the quality systems of firms that wish to do business in EEC member states. Most Military contractors and suppliers to many commercial businesses will be required to demonstrate compliance to ISO 9000 requirements, usually through a registration/certification process. Different organizations throughout the world are authorized to conduct quality system assessments and to provide certification. In the U.S. ASQC provides this service through their Registrar Accreditation Board.

(see section I.A.2 Domestic and international quality standards)

2. *The Malcolm Baldrige National Quality Award provides:*
   a. *a set of procedures designed to provide outstanding quality.*
   b. *a list of requirements that, if met, will result in the certification of the company to provide goods and services to the federal government.*
   c. *an award given by the Department of Defense to deserving suppliers for outstanding quality.*
   d. *recognition U.S. companies which excel in quality achievement and quality management.*

   The correct choice is *d.* The Malcolm Baldrige National Quality Award recognizes U.S. companies which have attained a high level of quality excellence and thereby competitive advantage in domestic and world marketplaces. Choice *a* is not correct because the Baldrige award is non-descriptive. The prospective CQE should obtain a free copy of the current application guidelines from the National Institute of Standards and Technology at 1-301-975-2036; quantities are available from ASQC for a nominal price.
   (see section I.A.3 Quality philosophies)

3. *Total quality management (TQM) is:*
   a. *100% inspection.*
   b. *a method applied to critical items to assure their complete reliability.*
   c. *the approach used by quality departments of suppliers to the department of defense.*
   d. *none of the above.*

   The correct choice is *d.* In a press release in June 1991, ASQC describes TQM as a customer-driven, process-improvement approach to management. The TQM committee of ASQC's Quality Management Division provides the following contrast of TQM and traditional management.

TRADITIONAL	TQM
Bottom line emphasis	Quality orientation
Meet specifications	Continuous improvement
Get product out	Satisfy customer requirements
Short term focus	Long term mission
Delegated quality responsibility	Management led improvement
Defect detection	Defect prevention
People as cost burdens	People as assets
Independent work	Teamwork
Minimum cost suppliers	Quality partner suppliers
Departmentalized activities	Cross-functional team efforts
Management by edict	Employee empowerment
Sequential engineering	Simultaneous engineering
Gut-feel decisions	Data-driven decisions
Management by objectives	Management by planning

D. ANSWERS TO SELECTED PAST EXAM QUESTIONS

1. *In preparing a Quality Policy concerning a product line for your company you should* **not**:

   a. *specify the means by which quality performance is measured.*

   b. *develop criteria for identifying risk situations, and specify whose approval is required when there are known risks.*

   c. *load the policy with procedural matters or ordinary functional responsibilities.*

   d. *identify responsibilities for dispositioning defective hardware.*

   e. *answers 2 and 4 above.*

   (Answer: d.)

2. *A quality program has the best foundation for success when it is initiated by:*
   a. *a certified quality engineer.*
   b. *contractual requirements.*
   c. *chief executive of company.*
   d. *production management.*
   e. *an experienced quality manager.*
   (Answer: c.)

3. *Who has the initial responsibility for manufactured product quality?*
   a. *the inspector.*
   b. *the vice president.*
   c. *the operator.*
   d. *the quality manager.*
   (Answer: c.)

4. *There are two basic aspects of product quality:*
   a. *in-process and finished product quality.*
   b. *appraisal costs and failure costs.*
   c. *quality of design and quality of conformance.*
   d. *impact of machines and impact of men.*
   (Answer: c.)

5. *The most important measure of outgoing quality needed by managers is product performance as viewed by:*
   a. *the customer.*
   b. *the final inspector.*
   c. *production.*
   d. *marketing.*
   (Answer: a.)

6. *Much managerial decision making is based on comparing actual performance with:*
    a. personnel ratio.
    b cost of operations.
    c. number of complaints.
    d. standards of performance.
    (Answer: d.)

7. *When giving instructions to those who will perform a task, the communication process is completed:*
    a. when the worker goes to his work station to do the task.
    b. when the person giving the instruction has finished talking.
    c. when the worker acknowledges these instructions by describing how he will perform the task.
    d. when the worker says that he understands the instructions.
    (Answer: c.)

8. *Studies have shown that the most effective communications method for transferring information is:*
    a. oral only.
    b. written only.
    c. combined written and oral.
    d. bulletin board.
    (Answer: c. See section I.A.4 Communication and presentation skills)

9. *In geometric dimensioning and tolerancing the symbol* M *means:*
    a. maximum material condition.
    b. use a micrometer to check.
    c. machined surface.
    d. measure at this point.
    (Answer: a. See section I.A.5 Interpretation of diagrams, schematics, drawings or blueprints)

10. *Specifying a tolerance by +0.000, -0.001 is known as:*
   a. *bilateral tolerance.*
   b. *limit dimensioning.*
   c. *manufacturing limits.*
   d. *unilateral tolerance.*
   *(Answer: **d**. See section I.A.5 Interpretation of diagrams, schematics, drawings or blueprints)*

II

Quality Practices and Applications

A. SOLUTIONS TO SELECTED EXERCISES FOUND IN *THE COMPLETE GUIDE TO THE CQE*

1. *Describe the application of Maslow's hierarchy of needs to a quality improvement team whose members include a machine operator paid the minimum wage, a new engineer, and an experienced department manager.*

   It is likely that each of these individuals are at different points in Maslow's hierarchy. The machine operator is likely motivated by physiological needs, the engineer by safety or social needs and the manager by ego or self-actualization needs.

   (see section II.A.1 Motivation theories and principles)

2. *Dr. Deming once stated that employee satisfaction could not be achieved solely by increasing the pay of the employee. Explain this statement using Herzberg's hygiene theory.*

   Herzberg lists salary as a hygiene factor. Hygiene factors affect dissatisfaction but not satisfaction. Thus, if salary is a source of employee dissatisfaction, then raising salaries will reduce dissatisfaction. However, according to Herzberg, this will not lead to satisfaction.

   (see section II.A.1 Motivation theories and principles)

3. *Manager A believes that employees must be carefully supervised to prevent them from taking advantage of the company. Manager B believes that once an employee understands the firm's mission, little supervision is necessary. Manager C believes that employees would like to do a better job, but that the management systems make it difficult for them to do so. Match these three manager's beliefs with theories X, Y and Z.*

Manager A = Theory X,

Manager B = Theory Z,

Manager C = Theory Y.

(see section II.A.1 Motivation theories and principles)

4. *Describe the three key items necessary to define a problem as "operator controllable."*

1. The operators know what they are supposed to do.

2. The operators know what they are actually doing.

3. The operators have the responsibility, authority, skill and tools necessary to correct the problems.

(see section II.A.2 Barriers to implementation of successful quality improvement efforts)

5. *List two methods that can be used to reduce inadvertent human errors and provide examples of each.*

Fool-proofing, automation (full or partial), ergonomics.

(see section II.A.2 Barriers to implementation of successful quality improvement efforts)

6. *List the three different types of human errors and provide examples of each.*

Inadvertent errors, technique errors, and willful errors.

(see section II.A.2 Barriers to implementation of successful quality improvement efforts)

7. *Describe how the structure of modern organizations creates barriers to change.*

    The gist of the response should be that by dividing responsibility and authority hierarchically and among several departments, the modern organization leads to destructive competition and discourages systems thinking.

    (see section II.A.2 Barriers to implementation of successful quality improvement efforts)

8. *Define the term "effective group."*

    An effective group is one where the group obtains results superior to those the members of the group would achieve acting individually.

    (see section II.A.3–5 regarding Teams)

9. *A quality improvement team has members that include hourly employees and senior level executives. What is the likely effect of this?*

    This violates the principle of approximately equal power and influence. It is likely to lead to failure to obtain distributed participation and leadership.

    (see section II.A.3–5 regarding Teams)

10. *Discuss why the consensus technique produces better decisions than conflict-avoidance techniques such as voting.*

    The consensus technique tends to produce convergence on the best decision by drawing out all of the relevant facts and opinions. The consensus technique also produces decisions which are supported by the entire group. Voting, and other conflict-avoidance techniques, tend to produce mediocre choices because they short-circuit discussion. Conflict-avoidance methods do not guarantee commitment from all members.

    (see section II.A.3–5 regarding Teams)

11. *Name the four stages in group development, describe the characteristics of each stage, and discuss the role of the leader in each stage.*
    (see section II.A.3–5 regarding Teams)

12. *Discuss the difference between group task roles and group maintenance roles.*
    (see section II.A.3–5 regarding Teams)

13. *Bob is constantly disrupting the team meetings with off-color jokes and irrelevant comments. As team leader, how would you deal with this situation?*

    The appropriate response is to confront Bob's behavior directly. This should be done, tactfully but firmly, at the time the counterproductive behavior occurs.
    (see section II.A.3–5 regarding Teams)

14. *Discuss management's responsibilities to quality improvement teams.*

    Management should provide an environment conducive to progress. It should also assure that teams have the correct membership, the authority and resources needed to succeed. Management should monitor the team's progress and remove obstacles encountered by the team.
    (see section II.A.3–5 regarding Teams)

15. *List at least two examples of product or service features for each quality level described by the Kano model.*

    Basic quality: windshield wipers on an automobile.
    Expected quality: rear windshield washers on a van.
    Exciting quality: rear seats in a van that "disappear" at the push of a button. Note: this feature does not, to my knowledge, exist. However, if it were offered my wife would be excited by it!
    (see section II.B Quality planning)

16. *Describe benchmarking and discuss some potential pitfalls if bench-marking is the sole means of goal-setting.*

   Benchmarking involves breaking work down into processes and identifying the best performer of the process. If benchmarking is the only goal-setting method used it will lead to performance that always follows the leader.
   (see section II.B Quality planning)

17. *Name two objectives of process qualification and validation.*

   1. Identify those process that are capable of meeting requirements;
   2. assuring that capable processes are actually performing at the level which they are capable.
   (see section II.B Quality planning)

18. *Describe the four phases of a QFD study.*

   The organization phase, the descriptive phase, the breakthrough phase and the implementation phase.
   (see section II.B Quality planning)

19. *Describe the house of quality.*

   The house of quality is a graphical device that links customer requirements directly to business processes. It also displays additional information on the relationship of the various processes to one another, on the competition, and on the relative importance of the processes in meeting the customer's requirements.
   (see section II.B Quality planning)

20. *Compare the quality planning approaches of Akao, Feigenbaum and Juran.*

   (see section II.B.4 Data collection and review of customer expectations, ...)

21. *What is the purpose of off-line analysis of computer reports?*

   (see section II.C Quality information systems)

22. *Name some of the advantages of digital archiving.*
   (see section II.C Quality information systems)

23. *A firm wishes to develop a vendor quality policy. Discuss the responsibilities of the product design, purchasing and quality departments in creating the policy.*

   Figure II.6 (pg. 91) in *The Complete Guide to the CQE* can be used as a guide. The student should discuss specific tasks each department is accountable for, for example, product design delivers detailed product descriptions, purchasing processes requisitions and prepares purchase orders which incorporate the appropriate requirements, quality per-forms systems audits, etc.
   (see section II.D Supplier management)

24. *Write a paragraph supporting the following position: multiple suppliers should be used for critical components.*
   (see section II.D Supplier management)

26. *Describe desk surveys.*
   (see section II.D Supplier management)

27. *List the steps involved in vendor quality planning.*
   (see section II.D Supplier management)

28. *Analyze the following data and discuss the results.*

PERFORMANCE	MEASURE	WEIGHT
Quality	% of lots accepted	5
Cost	100*(lowest cost/cost)	4
Delivery	% on-time shipments	3

The ratings calculations for 3 hypothetical suppliers is shown below.

VENDOR	% LOTS ACCEPTED	PRICE	% ON-TIME DELIVERIES
A	100	$55	95
B	95	70	100
C	85	50	95

Solution: The scores are: Vendor A = 1148, Vendor B = 1060, Vendor C = 1080.

(see section II.D Supplier management)

29. **Describe the basic types of quality audits.**

    Systems audits, product audits and process audits.

    (see section II.E Quality audit)

30. **How does a product audit differ from inspection?**

    (see section II.E Quality audit)

31. **Explain the difference between customer/supplier audits and third party audits.**

    (see section II.E Quality audit)

32. **Discuss the following: pre-award audits, surveillance audit, problem resolution audit.**

    (see section II.E Quality audit)

33. **Are the opinions of the auditor ever allowed in a formal audit report? If so, what guidelines should the auditor follow in reporting opinions?**

    Yes, auditor opinions are allowed provided they are clearly identified as opinions and supported by the facts. The more negative the opinion, the greater the supporting evidence required.

    (see section II.E Quality audit)

34. *Discuss the role of the senior auditor.*
    Senior auditors are generally responsible for coordinating the activities of the audit team and for assembling and reviewing the completed audit report.
    (see section II.E Quality audit)

35. *What is the final proof of the effectiveness of a corrective action?*
    It achieves the desired result.
    (see section II.E Quality audit)

36. *Contrast quality audit and quality survey.*
    Quality audits are formal structured evaluations of systems, products or processes conducted by independent personnel. Quality surveys are less formal reviews and are often performed by personnel in the area with findings reported to their own management. Survey reports, if prepared at all, are less formal than audit reports.
    (see section II.E Quality audit)

37. *Identify the four categories of quality costs.*
    Prevention, appraisal, internal failure, external failure.
    (see section II.F Cost of Quality)

38. *Determine the quality cost category for the following:*
    a. ISO 9000 certification audit expense
    b. cost of replacing a defective part on units in the field
    c. salaries of quality engineers
    d. process capability study
    e. scrap material.
       a. appraisal
       b. external failure
       c. cannot determine the cost category without knowing the specific activities of the engineers

d. prevention

e. internal failure.

(see section II.F Cost of Quality)

39. **A firm is spending the following amounts: prevention 5%, appraisal 25%, internal failure 30%, external failure 40%. What conclusion can be reached based on these figures?**

Without additional information it isn't possible to reach a conclusion regarding the proper allocation of quality costs. In a traditional mass-produced manufacturing operation these figures would suggest too little is being spent on prevention and appraisal, resulting in excessive failure costs.

(see section II.F Cost of Quality)

40. **Prepare a Pareto diagram from the following data:**

PROBLEM	$ SCRAP
Scratches	$1,500
Paint blisters	$657
Paint chipped	$1,709
Off-color	$150
Runs	$253
Other	$1,650

The Pareto diagram has certain properties: the data are sorted from the largest category to smallest (except "other" which is always the last category regardless of size), the left axis is scaled using the problem units (e.g., dollars) and it must start with 0 and include the total, the right axis is in percent and goes from 0% to 100%, bars are drawn to present the individual problems, a line is drawn representing the cumulative problem. The student should be corrected if they produce an ordinary bar chart or if their left axis is scaled to the largest category instead of to the total.

Pareto diagram from the above data.

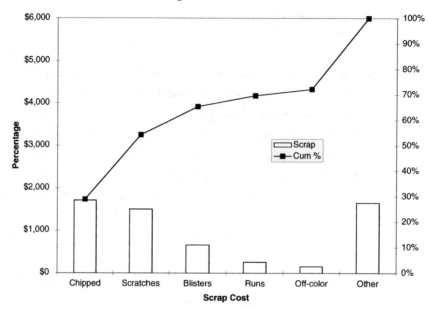

(see section II.G.1 Quality tools)

41. Describe three types of cause and effect diagrams.

Dispersion analysis type, production process class, cause enumeration type.
(see section II.G.1 Quality tools)

42. How does the CEDAC approach differ from traditional cause-and-effect diagrams?

CEDAC stands for cause-and-effect diagrams with the addition of cards. It differs from traditional diagrams in that it uses cards with descriptive comments and phrases rather than the short descriptions of traditional diagrams.
(see section II.G.1 Quality tools)

43. *Prepare a flowchart that describes the process of preparing for an examination in quality engineering.*
    (see section II.G.1 Quality tools)

44. *What is the fundamental purpose of a control chart?*
    To operationally define a special cause of variation in a process.
    (see section II.G.1 Quality tools)

45. *What are the three properties of a distribution?*
    Location, spread and shape.
    (see section II.G.1 Quality tools)

46. *Compare and contrast a strategy of process control/continuous improvement versus a strategy of zero defects.*
    Process control aims at, ultimately, reducing variation around a target value to zero. This may produce a process that far exceeds requirements. Zero defects stops as soon as the minimum requirement is met. In general, minimum cost is not at zero defects.
    (see section II.G.1 Quality tools)

47. *Compare and contrast the "goalpost" model and the Taguchi loss function.*
    This is essentially the same discussion as process control versus zero defects. The goalpost mental model leads to a zero defects strategy while the Taguchi loss function leads to process control and continuous improvement.

48. *Prepare a scatter diagram using the following data:*

PART	1	2	3	4	5	6	7	8	9	10
MICROMETER	105	107	110	115	117	119	123	125	128	130
CALIPER	103	106	108	114	115	117	121	124	126	129

(see section II.G.1 Quality tools)

49. *Create a histogram from the frequency table below. Discuss the information contained in the histogram.*

SIZE (MM)	25.0	25.1	25.2	25.3	25.4	25.5	25.6	25.7	25.8	25.9
FREQUENCY	30	45	100	90	60	55	45	30	10	2

Histogram created from the above data.

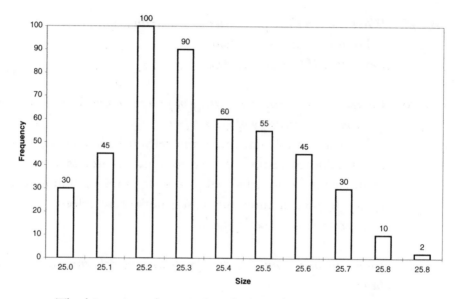

The histogram shows a distribution that is asymmetrical, it appears to have a positive skew. There do not appear to be any outliers. The mode is at 25.2. The mean will be greater than the mode due to the positive skew; the mean, computed from the frequency table, is approximately 25.34.

(see section II.G.1 Quality tools)

50. *Describe why the affinity diagram is called a data reduction technique.*
    (see section II.G.2 Management tools)

51. *Select a process familiar to you and, following the procedure in II.G.2, develop an affinity diagram.*
(*see section II.G.2 Management tools*)

52. *You are planning a picnic. Create an activity network diagram (arrow diagram) of this project.*
(*see section II.G.2 Management tools*)

B. DETAILED SOLUTIONS TO SELECTED PAST EXAM QUESTIONS

1. *An essential technique in making training programs effective is to:*
   a. *set group goals.*
   b. *have training classes which teach skills and knowledge required.*
   c. *feed back to the employee meaningful measures of his performance.*
   d. *post results of performance before and after the training program.*
   e. *set individual goals instead of group goals.*

   The only choice that is truly essential to effective training is *c*. One could debate choices *a* or *e*, and choice *e* might even be counterproductive. Choice *b* implies that effective training requires classroom teaching, which isn't necessarily so.
   (*see section II.A Human resource management*)

2. *Select the non-hygienic motivator, as defined by Maslow.**
   a. *salary increases.*
   b. *longer vacations.*
   c. *improved medical plan.*
   d. *sales bonuses.*
   e. *performance recognition.*

   Choice *e* is obviously correct. All other choices are hygienic motivators. *Actually, this is Herzberg's theory, not Maslow's.
   (*see section II.A Human resource management*)

3. *The famous Hawthorne study provided the following clinical evidence regarding the factors that can increase work group productivity:*
   a. *attention and recognition are more important than working conditions.*
   b. *productivity did not change significantly under any of the test conditions.*
   c. *informal group pressures set a production "goal."*
   d. *people with higher capabilities are bored with routine jobs.*
   e. *work station layout is critical to higher productivity.*

   The Hawthorne experiment involved a study where the working environment was changed for a selected group and the effect of the change was evaluated. The study found that the group's productivity improved *regardless of how the environment was changed!* The conclusion was that the improvement was the result of the special attention and recognition the selected groups received, choice *a*.
   (see section II.A Human resource management)

4. *Which one of these human management approaches has led to the practice of job enrichment?*
   a. *Skinner.*
   b. *Maslow.*
   c. *Herzberg's "Hygiene Theory."*
   d. *McGregor.*

   Herzberg's Hygiene Theory postulates that "satisfiers" and "dissatisfiers" are not opposites, rather they are separate scales altogether. "Satisfiers" are motivators that can result in improved performance. Dissatisfiers are "hygiene factors" that must be dealt with if motivation is to be effective. Some examples are shown below.

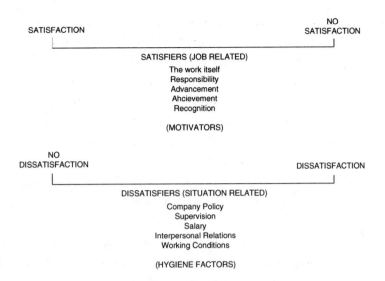

SATISFACTION   NO
                                                    SATISFACTION

SATISFIERS (JOB RELATED)
The work itself
Responsibility
Advancement
Ahcievement
Recognition

(MOTIVATORS)

NO
DISSATISFACTION   DISSATISFACTION

DISSATISFIERS (SITUATION RELATED)
Company Policy
Supervision
Salary
Interpersonal Relations
Working Conditions

(HYGIENE FACTORS)

Herzberg's hygiene theory.

While choice *c* is correct here, it is important that you review the theories of Skinner, Maslow, and McGregor as well. B.F. Skinner is a behaviorist who studied operant conditioning. Maslow is famous for his need hierarchy (below).

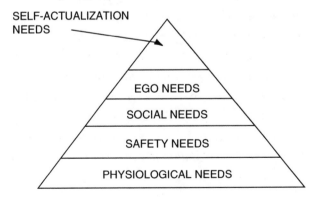

SELF-ACTUALIZATION
NEEDS

EGO NEEDS

SOCIAL NEEDS

SAFETY NEEDS

PHYSIOLOGICAL NEEDS

Need Hierarchy, A. S. Maslow, Brandeis University.

McGregor is known for theories X and Y:

Theory X—Employees are basically greedy, lazy, and uncooperative. Motivation should be in the form of pay penalties and incentives, disciplinary action, etc.

Theory Y—Employees are self-motivated; but they may lack the proper training and tools to do their job.

(see section II.A Human resource management)

5. *Extensive research into the results of quality motivation has shown that:*
   a. *the supervisor's attitude towards his people is of little long term con sequence.*
   b. *motivation is too nebulous to be correlated with results.*
   c. *motivation is increased when employees set their own goals.*
   d. *motivation is increased when management sets challenging goals slightly beyond the attainment of the better employees.*

   Choices *a*, *b*, and *d* have been shown to be *false*. Choice *c* is correct.

   (see section II.A Human resource management)

6. *Which of the following is* **not** *a management initiated error?*
   a. *the imposition of conflicting priorities.*
   b. *the lack of operator capacity.*
   c. *management indifference or apathy.*
   d. *conflicting quality specifications.*
   e. *work space, equipment and environment.*

   If we assume that "lack of operator capacity" means the operator is inherently incapable of performing acceptably in spite of adequate training and resources, then choice *b* is correct.

   (see section II.B Quality planning)

7. *Which of the following does not generate product-quality characteristics?*
   a. designer.
   b. inspector.
   c. machinist.
   d. equipment engineer.

   Inspectors do not *generate* quality characteristics; they merely compare them to operational standards. Choice *b* is correct.
   (see section II.B Quality planning)

8. *A quality control program is considered to be:*
   a. a collection of quality control procedures and guidelines.
   b. a step by step list of all quality control check points.
   c. a summary of company quality control policies.
   d. a system of activities to provide quality of products and service.

   A quality control *program* is more than just procedures, lists, or policy summaries. It is the system of all activities that provide quality products and services. Choice *d* is best.
   (see section II.B Quality planning)

9. *When planning a total quality system, one key objective is to provide a means of guaranteeing "the maintenance of product integrity." Which of the following quality system provisions is designed to **most** directly provide such a guarantee?*
   a. drawing and print control.
   b. calibration and maintenance of test equipment.
   c. identification and segregation of non-conforming material.
   d. specification change control.

   The key words here are *most direct*. While all of the choices provide a means of guaranteeing the maintenance of product integrity, identification and segregation of non-conforming material, choice *c*, is the most direct means.
   (see section II.B Quality planning)

10. *The "quality function" of a company is best described as:*

a. the degree to which the company product conforms to a design or specification.

b. that collection of activities through which "fitness for use" is achieved.

c. the degree to which a class or category of product possesses satisfaction for people generally.

d. all of the above.

The "quality function" is analogous to the "quality program" discussed in question 59. The best choice is *b*.

(see section II.B Quality planning)

11. *The advantage of a written procedure is:*

a. it provides flexibility in dealing with problems.

b. unusual conditions are handled better.

c. it is a perpetual coordination device.

d. coordination with other departments is not required.

The only valid choice is *c*. None of the others are advantages of written procedures, in fact they are among the *disadvantages* of written procedures!

(see section II.B Quality planning)

12. *In preparing a Product Quality Policy for your company, you should do all of the following except:*

a. specify the means by which quality performance is measured.

b. develop criteria for identifying risk situations and specify whose approval is required when there are known risks.

c. include procedural matters and functional responsibilities.

d. state quality goals.

Choice *c* is not appropriate material for a quality *policy*.

(see section II.B Quality planning)

13. *Which of the following is most important when calibrating a piece of equipment?*
    a. calibration sticker.
    b. maintenance history card.
    c. standard used.
    d. calibration interval.

    If the calibration standard is inadequate the other 3 items are meaningless. Choice *c* is correct.
    (see section II.B Quality planning)

14. *The quality assurance function is comparable to which of the following other business functions in concept?*
    a. general accounting.
    b. cost accounting.
    c. audit accounting.
    d. all of the above.

    Quality assurance and audit accounting have several similarities. In both activities we seek independent verification by qualified auditors that an adequate system exists and is being followed. Choice *c* is correct.
    (see section II.B Quality planning)

15. *Complaint indices should:*
    a. recognize the degree of dissatisfaction as viewed by the customer.
    b. provide a direct input to corrective action.
    c. not necessarily be based on field complaints or dollar values of claims paid or on service calls.
    d. ignore life cycle costs.

    A valid complaint index must somehow measure the degree of customer dissatisfaction. A mildly dissatisfied customer may still buy your product; an extremely dissatisfied customer may discourage others from buying your product. Thus choice *a* is best.

    The only possible alternate choice is choice *b*. It can be argued that while complaint indices can be *used* in corrective action, they don't in and of themselves provide *direct* input into this process. In fact, the input is often quite indirect.

(see section II.C Quality information systems)

16. *Effective Automated Data Processing is:*
    a. a process which uses punch cards to sort, compile and analyze data.
    b. a process in which computers are used to analyze data.
    c. a process, largely self-regulating, in which information is handled with a minimum of human effort and intervention.
    d. a process in which records are classified, sorted, computed, summarized, transmitted and stored.
    e. none of the above.

Choice *c* is clearly best. Choices *a*, *b*, and *d* describe attributes of old automated data processing systems, but these systems could well be quite ineffective.

(see section II.C Quality information systems)

17. *Analysis of data on all product returns is important because:*
    a. failure rates change with length of product usage.
    b. changes in design and in customer use are often well reflected.
    c. immediate feedback and analysis of product performance becomes available.
    d. all of the above.
    e. none of the above.

Analysis of data on all product returns is important for all the reasons given, thus choice *d* should be selected. Note that choice *e* *can't* be right because "all of the above" is one of the above!

(see section II.C Quality information systems)

18. *Quality data, which are regularly obtained but not used, should be:*
    a. *analyzed periodically by an expert statistician to glean as much information as possible.*
    b. *discontinued to save time and money.*
    c. *stored until such time as the need arises.*
    d. *processed by computer and summary reports issued regularly to interested persons.*

    Some organizations spend huge sums of money handling quality data that is never used. If the data are truly important, it is unlikely that this would occur "regularly." Useless data is useless even if analyzed by a statistician or processed by a computer or saved; the famous "garbage in garbage out" syndrome. The best choice is *b*.
    (see section II.C Quality information systems)

19. *The primary reason for evaluating and maintaining surveillance over a supplier's quality program is to:*
    a. *perform product inspection at source.*
    b. *eliminate incoming inspection cost.*
    c. *motivate suppliers to improve quality.*
    d. *make sure the supplier's quality program is functioning effectively.*

    While all choices are valid reasons for evaluating and maintaining surveillance over a supplier's quality program, choice *d* is the *primary* reason.
    (see section II.D Supplier management)

20. *Incoming-material inspection is based most directly on:*
    a. *design requirements.*
    b. *purchase order requirements.*
    c. *manufacturing requirements.*
    d. *customer use of the end product.*

    Again the key words are *most directly*, and choice *b* is the best.
    (see section II.D Supplier management)

21. *The most important step in vendor certification is to*
    a. *obtain copies of vendor's handbook.*
    b. *familiarize vendor with quality requirements.*
    c. *analyze vendor's first shipment.*
    d. *visit the vendor's plant.*

    If the vendor isn't familiar with your requirements, chances are he won't meet them, even if he can. Choice *b* is correct.
    . (see section II.D Supplier management)

22. *Which of the following may be considered a justification for reinspection by the contractor of a lot which has been verified as nonconforming by the inspector?*
    a. *belief by the contractor that the random samples did not constitute a true picture of the lot.*
    b. *the fact that the contractor had not produced to these specifications before.*
    c. *discovery that the scales used for inspection were out of adjustment.*
    d. *none of the above.*

    Only choice *c* is justification. Choice *a* is a matter of (biased) opinion, choice *b* is irrelevant.
    (see section II.D Supplier management)

23. *A quality audit program should begin with:*
    a. *a study of the quality documentation system.*
    b. *an evaluation of the work being performed.*
    c. *a report listing findings, the action taken, and recommendations.*
    d. *a charter of policy, objectives, and procedures.*
    e. *a follow-up check on the manager's response to recommendations.*

    The key word here is *begin*. Choice *d* describes activities that occur at the start of a quality audit program. The other choices describe actual audit activities.
    (see section II.E Quality audit)

24. *Auditing of a quality program is most effective on a:*
    a. *quarterly basis, auditing all characteristics on the checklist.*
    b. *periodic unscheduled basis, auditing some of the procedures.*
    c. *monthly basis, auditing selected procedures.*
    d. *continuing basis, auditing randomly selected procedures.*
    e. *continually specified time period basis, frequency adjustable, auditing randomly selected procedures.*

    The correct choice is *e*.

(see section II.E Quality audit)

25. *An inspection performance audit is made of eight inspectors in an area of complex assembly, all doing similar work. Seven inspectors have an average monthly acceptance rate of 86 to 92%, one inspector has an average rate of 72% with approximately four times the daily variation as the others. As inspection supervisor you should, based on this audit,*
    a. *promote the 72% inspector as he is very conscientious.*
    b. *discipline the 72% inspector as he is creating needless rework and wasted time.*
    c. *initiate a special investigation of inspection and manufacturing performance.*
    d. *discipline the other seven inspectors as they are not "cracking down."*

    The audit result indicates only that a *problem* exists, it tells us nothing about the *cause* of the problem. Choices *a*, *b*, and *d* all presume information that was not given. The difference could be in the training, gauging, lighting, or any number of other things. Only choice *c* is reasonable.

(see section II.E Quality audit)

26. *The quality audit could be used to judge all of the following* except:
    a. a prospective vendor's capability for meeting quality standards.
    b. the adequacy of a current vendor's system for controlling quality.
    c. the application of a specification to a unique situation.
    d. the adequacy of a company's own system for controlling quality.

    Choice *c* is clearly *not* an appropriate activity for a quality audit. Quality audits are intended to provide information on fundamental problems, not unique situations. If this is not immediately obvious, you should reread the reference materials.
    (see section II.E Quality audit)

27. *Audit inspectors should report to someone who is independent from:*
    a. middle management.
    b. marketing.
    c. inspection supervision.
    d. production staff.

    One of the guiding principles of quality audit is that they are carried out by trained or experienced persons who are independent, i.e. they have no responsibility for the conduct of the activity being audited. Self-evaluations and quality surveys are not the same as quality audits. This principle makes choice *c* correct.
    (see section II.E Quality audit)

28. *The term "quality audit" can refer to the appraisal of the quality system of:*
    a. an entire plant or company.
    b. one product.
    c. one major quality activity.
    d. any of the above.

    The term quality audit is used in a very broad sense, choice *d* is correct.
    (see section II.E Quality audit)

29. *You would normally* not *include data from which of the following investigations in quality auditing?*
    a. examination of all items produced.
    b. examination of customer needs and the adequacy of design specifications in reflecting these needs.
    c. examination of vendor product specifications and monitoring procedures.
    d. examination of customer quality complaints and adequacy of corrective action.

    The purpose of an audit is to assure that an effective system has been developed and is being followed. Choice *a* does not fit this purpose.
    (see section II.E Quality audit)

30. *In order to be effective, the Quality Audit function should ideally be:*
    a. an independent organizational segment in the Quality Control function.
    b. an independent organizational segment in the Production Control function.
    c. an independent organizational segment in Manufacturing operations function.
    d. all of the above.

    The objectivity of the audit function is better assured by having the function report independently of the groups being audited. Choice *a* provides this objectivity.
    (see section II.E Quality audit)

31. *Which of the following quality system provisions is of the greatest concern when preparing an audit check list for a quality system audit?*
    a. drawing and print control.
    b. make-up of the MRB (Material Review Board).
    c. training level of inspectors.
    d. optimization of production processes.
    e. calibration of test equipment.

    The official answer is choice *e*; it may be argued that the other choices are not really quality systems per se.
    (see section II.E Quality audit)

32. *The following are reasons why an independent audit of actual practice versus procedures should be performed periodically.*
    1. Pressures may force the supervisor to deviate from approved procedures.
    2. The supervisor may not have time for organized follow-up or adherence to procedures.
    3. Supervisors are not responsible for implementing procedures.
    a. 1 and 2 only
    b. 2 and 3 only
    c. 1 and 3 only
    d. 1, 2 and 3

    The best choice is *a*, 1 and 2 only. All other choices are incorrect since they include 3 and 3 is not true.
    (see section II.E Quality audit)

33. *A Vendor Quality Survey:*
   a. is used to predict whether a potential vendor can meet quality requirements.
   b. is an audit of a vendor's product for a designated period of time.
   c. is always conducted by Quality Control personnel only.
   d. reduces cost by eliminating the need for receiving inspection of the surveyed vendor's product.

   The correct answer is choice *a*. Just how accurate this prediction is has been debated for many years. Choices *b*, *c*, and *d* are often untrue. *(see section II.E Quality audit)*

34. *A certain part is produced in lot quantities of 1,000. Prior history shows that 90% of the production lots are 1% defective or better, but the remaining 10% range between 5% and 10% defective. A defective part costs $5 to repair at this point, but the same defect will average $80 if allowed to be installed in the next higher assembly. Inspection at the part level costs $1.50 per part, and rejected lots will be sorted at your expense. What inspection plan would you specify for this part?*
   a. 100% inspection.
   b. no inspection.
   c. n = 32, A = 1, R = 2 (single-sampling).
   d. n = 50, A = 0, R = 1 (single-sampling).
   e. n = 5, A = 1, R = 2 (single-sampling).

   The objective is to minimize the average total cost per lot, which is given by the equation

$$C = \$1.5 \times ATI + \$5 \times ATR + \$80 \times ADI$$

   where   ATI = Average total inspected per lot.

   ATR = Average total repaired per lot.

   ADI = Average defectives installed at a higher assembly per lot. We'll assume 5% are 5% defective and 5% are 10% defective.

With 100% Inspection

$$\text{ATI} = 1000$$

$$
\begin{aligned}
\text{ATR} &= .9(.01)(1000) + .05(.05)(1000) + .05(.10)(1000) \\
&= 1000\ [.9(.01) + .05(.05) + .05(.10)] \\
&= 16.5
\end{aligned}
$$

ADI = 0, assuming perfect inspection

and C = 1.5 (1000) + 5 (16.5) +80 (0) = *$1582.50*

With No Inspection

$$\text{ATI} = 0$$

$$\text{ATR} = 0$$

ADI = 16.5 (same as ATR above)

and C = 1.5 (0) + 5 (0) + 80 (16.5) = *$1320.00*

With n = 32, A = 1, R = 2

(Binomial distribution used to get probabilities)

$$
\begin{aligned}
\text{ATI} &= .9\ [32 + .04\ (1000{-}32)] + .05\ [32 + .48\ (1000{-}32)] \\
&\quad + .05\ [32 + .84\ (1000{-}32)] = 130.736
\end{aligned}
$$

$$\text{ATR} = 16.5 - 10.74 = 5.76$$

$$
\begin{aligned}
\text{ADI} &= [.9\ (.96)(.01) + .05(.52)(.05) + .05(.16)(.10)]\ 1000 \\
&= 10.74
\end{aligned}
$$

and C = 1.5(130.736) + 5(5.76) + 80(10.74) = *$1084.10*

Using similar methods for the other choices gives us the table below (slight variations exist due to rounding).

PLAN	ATI	ATR	ADI	COST
100% inspection	1000	16.5	0	$1,582.50
0% inspection	0	0	16.50	$1,320.00
n=32: A=1 , R=2	131.51	6.13	10.37	$1,057.73
n=50: A=0, R= 1	478.82	11.12	5.38	$1,204.23
n=5; A=1, R=2	11.05	.055	15.95	$1,295.13

The least cost scheme is choice *c*. Save such lengthy problems until you've answered all others.

(see section II.F Cost of quality, and sections III.B and III.F)

35. **For a typical month, 900D Manufacturing Company identified and reported the following quality costs:**

Inspection wages	*$ 12,000*
Quality planning	*4,000*
Source inspection	*2,000*
In-plant scrap and rework	*88,000*
Final product test	*110,000*
Retest and troubleshooting	*39,000*
Field warranty cost	*205,000*
Evaluation and processing of deviation requests	*6,000*

What is the total failure cost for this month?

a. $244,000
b. $151,000
c. $261,000
d. $205,000
e. $332,000

The *failure costs* are

ITEM	AMOUNT
In-plant scrap and rework	$ 88,000
Retest and troubleshooting	$39,000
Field warranty cost	$205,000
TOTAL	$332,000

Choice *e*. (*Note:* Evaluation and processing of deviation requests is an appraisal cost.)

(see section II.F Cost of quality)

36. *(Refer to the previous question.)*

One year later, the monthly quality costs reported by 900D Manufacturing Company were as follows:

Inspection wage	$ 14,000
Quality planning	8,500
Source inspection	2,200
In-plant scrap and rework	51,000
Quality training	42,000
Audits	47,000
Final product test	103,000
Retest and troubleshooting	19,000
Field warranty cost	188,000
Evaluation & processing of deviation requests	4,500

Sales billed have increased 10% from the corresponding month of a year ago. How would you evaluate the effectiveness of 900D quality improvement program?

a. Quality costs are still too high.

b. Essentially no change in overall results.

c. Good improvement.

d. Still further improvement is unlikely.

e. Not enough information to evaluate.

Total Quality Costs—Year 1: $466,000

Total Quality Costs—Year 2: $479,200

Change = +2.8%

If our only comparison base is sales billed, then the increase in quality costs is smaller than would be expected. Thus choice c is correct. Keep in mind, however, that in the real world cost analysis is far more complex, usually involving several bases and breakdown of costs into various categories.

(see section II.F Cost of quality)

37. *If prevention costs are increased to pay for engineering work in quality control, and this results in a reduction in the number of product defects, this yields a reduction in:*
    a. appraisal costs.
    b. operating costs.
    c. quality costs.
    d. failure costs.
    e. manufacturing costs.

    Failure costs are defined as costs related to *defects*; choice *d* is most correct. This doesn't mean that the other costs listed won't change too, but the only costs we can be sure about are failure costs.
    (see section II.F Cost of quality)

38. *Analysis of quality costs consists of:*
    a. reviewing manpower utilization against standard.
    b. evaluating seasonal productivity.
    c. establishing management tools to determine net worth.
    d. examining each cost element in relation to other elements and the total.
    e. providing an accounting mechanism to spread costs over serviced areas.

    The analysis of quality costs is described best by choice *d*.
    (see section II.F Cost of quality)

39. *Assume that the cost data available to you for a certain period are limited to the following:*

Final test	$ 18,000
Loss on disposition of surplus stock	15,000
Field warranty costs	275,000
Scrap	150,000
Customer returns	25,000
Planning for inspection	16,000

The total of the quality costs is:
a. $499,000.
b. $484,000.
c. $468,000.
d. $193,000.

Choice *b* is correct. Loss on disposition of surplus stock is not a quality cost.

(see section II.F Cost of quality)

40. *Market based cost standards are guided by:*
a. *what others spend.*
b. *what we ought to spend.*
c. *marketing budget.*
d. *quality analysis forecast.*

Many, many companies base their expenditures on what others in similar circumstances spend. These are called "market base cost standards," choice *a*. The quality profession is familiar with market based *quality standards*, where the quality of one's product is judged compared to the quality of competing product.

(see section II.F Cost of quality)

41. *The cost of writing instructions and operating procedures for inspection and testing should be charged to:*
    a. prevention costs.
    b. appraisal costs.
    c. internal failure costs.
    d. external failure costs.

    Choice *a* is correct, tricky eh? A natural tendency is to classify these costs as appraisal costs. However, a review of the reference material, including the definitions provided in this solutions maunal, show clearly that these are prevention costs. Perhaps it is easier to understand if one considers the case where we are writing procedures for analyzing field failures. Obviously it would be absurd to call the cost of developing these procedures failure costs.
    (see section II.F Cost of quality)

42. *Which of the following activities is not normally charged as a preventive cost?*
    a. quality training.
    b. design and development of quality measurement equipment.
    c. quality planning.
    d. laboratory acceptance testing.

    Choice *d* describes an appraisal cost. Charges in this category would include work done, for example, by Underwriter's Laboratories.
    (see section II.F Cost of quality)

43. *In selecting a base for measuring quality costs, which of the following should be considered?*
    a. Is it sensitive to increases and decreases in production schedules?
    b. Is it affected by mechanization and the resulting lower direct labor costs?
    c. Is it affected by seasonal product sales?
    d. Is it oversensitive to material price fluctuations?
    e. All of the above.

The answer is *e*. One of the most widespread problems associated with any economic comparison of an indicator to a base is to determine whether an observed movement in the comparison index was due to a change in the indicator or a change in the base. Unfortunately, no easy formula exists to help you choose a base.
(see section II.F Cost of quality)

44. *Which of the following quality cost indices is likely to have the greatest appeal to top management as an indicator of relative cost?*
    a. quality cost per unit of product.
    b. quality cost per hour of direct production labor.
    c. quality cost per unit of processing cost.
    d. quality cost per unit of sales.
    e. quality cost per dollar of direct production labor.

    Top management is more accustomed to viewing most costs relative to sales than any of the other indices given. Thus choice *d* is best. However, other company groups (engineering, manufacturing, etc.) may find the costs relative to one of the other indices more useful.
    (see section II.F Cost of quality)

45. *Review of purchase orders for quality requirements falls into which one of the following quality cost segments?*
    a. prevention.
    b. appraisal.
    c. internal failures.
    d. external failures.

    Purchase order review is performed to reduce appraisal and failure costs, thus it is a prevention cost, choice *a*.
    (see section II.F Cost of quality)

46. *Failure costs include costs due to:*
  a. quality control engineering.
  b. inspection set-up for tests.
  c. certification of special-process suppliers.
  d. supplier analysis of non-conforming hardware.

  The choices can be categorized as follows:
  Choice *a*: Prevention.
  Choice *b*: Appraisal.
  Choice *c*: Prevention.
  Choice *d*: Failure.
  (see section II.F Cost of quality)

47. *Quality cost trend analysis is facilitated by comparing quality costs to:*
  a. manufacturing costs over the same time period.
  b. cash flow reports.
  c. appropriate measurement bases.
  d. QC department budget.

  As discussed in question 95, the appropriate measurement base varies with the cost category and the audience. Therefore choice *c* is best.
  (see section II.F Cost of quality)

48. *Which of the following is least likely to be reported as a failure-related cost?*
  a. sorting lots rejected by a sampling procedure.
  b. downtime caused by late delivery of a purchased part rejected by the supplier's final inspection.
  c. repair of field failures.
  d. retesting of a repaired product.

  While all of the costs shown are failure costs, common sense would indicate that choice *b* is least *likely to be reported* as a failure related cost.
  (see section II.F Cost of quality)

49. *The basic objective of a quality cost program is to:*
    a. *identify the source of quality failures.*
    b. *interface with the accounting department.*
    c. *improve the profit of your company.*
    d. *identify quality control department costs.*

    The *basic* objective of a quality cost program is profit improvement, choice *c*. A discussion of the relationship of quality costs and profits is given in Pyzdek, T., "The Impact of Quality Cost Reduction on Profits," *Quality Progress*, Oct. 1976.
    (see section II.F Cost of quality)

50. *Cost of calibrating test and inspection equipment would be included in:*
    a. *prevention cost.*
    b. *appraisal cost.*
    c. *failure cost.*
    d. *material-procurement cost.*

    Our cost category definitions clearly place these costs in the appraisal category, choice *b*.
    (see section II.F Cost of quality)

51. *In some instances, the ordinary cost-balance formula is not valid and cannot be applied because of the presence of vital intangibles. Such an intangible involves:*
    a. *safety of human beings.*
    b. *compliance with legislation.*
    c. *apparatus for collection of revenue.*
    d. *credit to marketing as new sales for warranty replacements.*
    e. *none of the above.*

    When human safety is at issue the analysis must extend beyond cost-benefit relationships and include, among other things, discussion of moral, ethical, and legal aspects of any decision. Choice *a* is correct.
    (see section II.F Cost of quality)

52. *When looking for existing sources of external failure cost data, which of the following is usually the best source available?*

    a. customer corrective action requests.

    b. salesmen's field reports.

    c. accounting reports on "sales of seconds" or "distressed merchandise."

    d. returned material reports.

    Based on my experience, I concur that the best source of external failure cost data (of the choices given) are returned material reports, choice *d*. However, I have found that excellent data usually exists on total warranty, including returned goods, field repair, etc.

    (see section II.F Cost of quality)

53. *The prime use of a control chart is to*

    a. detect assignable causes of variation in the process.

    b. detect nonconforming product.

    c. measure the performance of all quality characteristics of a process.

    d. detect the presence of random variation in the process.

    Choice *a* describes Walter Shewhart's main reason for inventing the control chart technique.

    (see section II.G.1 Quality tools)

C. SIMULATED EXAM QUESTIONS

1. *The graph shown is interpreted as follows:*

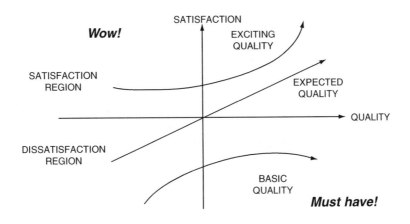

a. *Customer satisfaction is determined solely by the quantity of the product or service delivered.*

b. *Customer wants can be determined once and for all and used to design high quality products and services.*

c. *Customer wants, needs and expectations are dynamic and must be monitored continuously. Providing products or services that match the customer's expectations is not enough to assure customer satisfaction.*

d. *Customers will be satisfied if you supply them with products and services that meet their needs at a fair price.*

The figure, based on the Kano Model, describes a situation of dynamic customer perceptions which are influenced by many factors, including the competition. Choice *c* is correct. Studies of customer satisfaction have demonstrated convincingly that customer satisfaction is not solely determined by the manufacturer's perception of the quality of the product or service; conformance to engineering requirements is an inadequate standard of quality. As the figure demonstrates, competitive pressure will make today's *wow* features tomorrow's *must have* features. Customer expectations tend to increase steadily over time.

(see section II.B Quality planning)

2. *The search for industry best practices that lead to superior performance is called:*

a. *benchmarking.*

b. *market research.*

c. *total quality management.*

d. *outsourcing.*

The correct answer is *a*. Benchmarking was a key element of Xerox Corporation's strategy for recapturing lost markets through quality improvement, a strategy that led to their winning the Malcolm Baldrige National Quality Award in 1989.

(see section II.B Quality planning)

3. *The house of quality is produced by which of the following methods?*
    a. TQM.
    b. quality function deployment.
    c. affinity diagrams.
    d. ISO 9000.

    The correct answer is *b*. Quality function deployment (QFD) as a system for design of a product or service based on customer demands, a system that moves methodically from customer requirements to requirements for the products or services. QFD consists of four distinct phases:

    Organization phase—Management selects the product or service to be improved, the appropriate interdepartmental team, and defines the focus of the QFD study.

    Descriptive phase—The team defines the product or service from several different directions such as customer demands, functions, parts, reliability, cost, and so on.

    Breakthrough phase—The team selects areas for improvement and finds ways to make them better through new technology, new concepts, better reliability, cost reduction, etc., and monitors the bottleneck process.

    Implementation phase—The team defines the new product and how it will be manufactured.

    (see section II.C.5 Quality documentation systems)

4. *The interrelationship digraph, tree diagram and affinity diagram are examples of:*
    a. the 7 M tools.
    b. classical SPC tools.
    c. DOE techniques.
    d. none of the above.

    The three methods are a subset of what has come to be known as the 7 M tools, choice *a*.

    (see section II.G.2 Management tools)

D. ANSWERS TO SELECTED PAST EXAM QUESTIONS

1. *McGregor's theory X manager is typified as one who operates from the following basic assumption about people working for him (select the one best answer):*

   a. Performance can be improved through tolerance and trust.

   b. People have a basic need to produce.

   c. Status is more important than money.

   d. Self-actualization is the highest order of human need.

   e. People are lazy and are motivated by reward and punishment.

   *(Answer: **e**. See section II.A Human resource management)*

2. *Quality motivation in industry should be directed at:*

   a. manufacturing management

   b. procurement and engineering

   c. the quality assurance staff

   d. the working force

   e. all the above

   *(Answer: **e**. See section II.A Human resource management)*

3. *In order to instill the quality control employee with the desire to perform to his utmost and optimum ability, which of the following recognition for sustaining motivation has been found effective for most people?*

   a. recognition by issuance of monetary award

   b. verbal recognition publicly

   c. private verbal recognition

   d. public recognition, plus non-monetary award

   e. no recognition; salary he obtains is sufficient motivation

   *(Answer: **d**. See section II.A Human resource management)*

4. Which of the following methods used to improve employee efficiency and promote an atmosphere conducive to quality and profit is the most effective in the long run?

    a. offering incentives such as bonus, praise, profit sharing, etc.

    b. strict discipline to reduce mistakes, idleness, and sloppiness.

    c. combination of incentive and discipline to provide both reward for excellence and punishment for inferior performance.

    d. building constructive attitudes through development of realistic quality goals relating to both company and employee success

    e. all of the above provided emphasis is placed on attitude motivation, with incentive and discipline used with utmost caution.

    (Answer: e. See section II.A Human resource management)

5. The Quality Engineer should be concerned with the human factors of a new piece of in-house manufacturing equipment as well as its operational effects because it:

    a. may speed the line to the point where a visual operator inspection is impossible.

    b. may require the operator's undivided attention at the controls so the product cannot be fully seen

    c. may remove an operator formerly devoting some portion of time to inspection

    d. all of the above

    (Answer: d. See section II.A Human resource management)

6. The famous Hawthorne study provided which of the following clinical evidence regarding the factors that can increase work group productivity?

    a. attention and recognition is more important than working conditions.

    b. productivity did not change significantly under any of the test conditions.

c. informal group pressures set a production "goal."

d. people with higher capabilities are bored with routine jobs.

e. work station layout is critical to higher productivity.

(Answer: *a*. See section II.A Human resource management)

7. The technology for predicting human reliability in production process:

a. is inevitably correlated with monetary rewards.

b. is represented by the many motivation programs in effect.

c. is still in the developmental stages.

d. is based on the determination of the workmanship error rate.

(Answer:*c*. See section II.A Human resource management)

8. One of the most important techniques in making a training program effective is to:

a. give people meaningful measures of performance.

b. transmit all of the information that is even remotely related to the function.

c. set individual goals instead of group goals.

d. concentrate only on developing knowledge and skills needed to do a good job.

(Answer: *a*. See section II.A Human resource management)

9. The application of human factors in a plant production environment:

a. identifies reasons why errors are made.

b. is a practical example of using psychological techniques on workers.

c. is identified with a formal quality motivation program.

d. relates attitudes and prejudices among plant personnel.

(Answer: *a*. See section II.A Human resource management)

10. *The effective supervisor:*

    a. sees his role primarily as one of making people happy.

    b. sometimes does a job himself because he can do it better than others.

    c. has objectives of growth and increased profit by working through other people.

    d assumes the functions of planning, decision making and monitoring performance, but leaves personnel development to the personnel department.

    (Answer: c. See section II.A Human resource management)

11. *The purpose of a Quality Manual is to:*

    a. use it as a basis for every Quality decision

    b. standardize the methods and decisions of a department

    c optimize company performance in addition to improving the effectiveness of the Quality department

    d. make it possible to handle every situation in exactly the same manner

    (Answer: c. See section II.B Quality planning)

12. *Essential to the success of any Quality Control organization is the receipt of:*

    a. adequate and stable resources

    b. clear and concise project statements

    c. delegation of authority to accomplish the objective

    d. all of the above

    (Answer: d. See section II.B Quality planning)

13. *The first step and most important in establishing a good corporate quality plan is:*
    a. *determining customer requirements*
    b. *determining manufacturing process capabilities*
    c. *evaluating vendor quality system*
    d. *ensuring quality participation in design review*
    (Answer: a. See section II.B Quality planning)

14. *Some product specifications contain a section called "Quality Assurance" which contains the design engineer's requirements for acceptance testing The relationship between the acceptance test procedure for a product and the acceptance test portion of the quality assurance section of the specification for that product is:*
    a. *test procedure must require testing for the characteristics listed in the acceptance test portion of the specification and the quality engineer can add additional tests he believes necessary.*
    b. *test procedure must require testing for characteristics selected from the acceptance test portion of the specification but does not have to require testing for all such characteristics.*
    c. *test procedure must require testing for those and only those characteristics listed in the acceptance test portion of the specification.*
    d. *the acceptance test portion of the specification is a good general guide to the test procedure writer and the test procedure reviewer but is not mandatory in any way.*
    (Answer: a. See section II.B Quality planning)

15. *A quality manual:*
    a. *is a static document, best used for Public Relations purposes.*
    b. *is a benchmark against which current practice may be audited.*
    c. *is the responsibility of all company departments.*
    d. *should be approved only by the quality department.*
    e. *is not needed in most organizations.*
    (Answer: b. See section II.B Quality planning)

16. *In planning for quality, an important consideration at the start is:*
    a. the relation of the total cost of quality to the net sales.
    b. the establishment of a company quality policy or objective.
    c. deciding precisely how much money is to be spent.
    d. the selling of the quality program to top management.
    (Answer: **b**. *See section II.B Quality planning)*

17. *When planning the specifications for product quality in the so-called "mechanical" industries:*
    a. market research helps to establish economic tolerances.
    b. quality control develops products possessing qualities which meet customer needs.
    c. product research issues official product specifications.
    d. product design assumes prime responsibility for establishing economic tolerances.
    (Answer: **b**. *See section II.B Quality planning)*

18. *In the so-called "process" industries:*
    a. quality control has some responsibility in choosing the process.
    b. quality control may help to establish process tolerances.
    c. process development issues process specifications.
    d. all of the above.
    (Answer: **d**. *See section II.B Quality planning)*

19. *When planning the quality aspects of packing and shipping, it is* not *usual that the:*
    a. product design department specify packaging and shipping procedures.
    b. shipping department conduct packing and shipping operations.
    c. inspection department determine package specifications.
    d. inspection department check the adequacy of packing and shipping operations.
    (Answer: **c**. *See section II.B Quality planning)*

20. Establishing the quality policy for the company is typically the responsibility of:
    a. marketing department.
    b. top management.
    c. quality control.
    d. customer.
    (Answer: *b*. See section II.B Quality planning)

21. When a new manufacturing process is contemplated, an important reason for scheduling a trial production lot is:
    a. to prove engineering feasibility.
    b. to prove that the pilot plant results are the same as those in the production shop.
    c. to prove that the tools and processes can produce the product successfully with economic yields.
    d. that it is inexpensive.
    (Answer: *c*. See section II.B Quality planning)

22. In the pre-production phase of quality planning, an appropriate activity would be to:
    a. determine responsibility for process control.
    b. determine the technical depth of available manpower.
    c. establish compatible approaches for accumulation of process data.
    d conduct process capability studies to measure process expectations.
    (Answer: *b*. See section II.B Quality planning)

23. Process acceptance involves decision making with regard to:
    a. the type of equipment or machinery used to process items during manufacture.
    b. items not yet made; that is, approval of "first piece" and periodic checks during a production run.

c. items already made regardless of the technique used to control quality during processing.

d. acceptance sampling using MIL-STD-105E.

*(Answer: **b**. See section II.B Quality planning)*

24. *A fully developed position description for a Quality Engineer must contain clarification of:*

    a. responsibility.

    b. accountability.

    c. authority.

    d. answers a and c above.

    e. answers a, b and c above.

    *(Answer: **e**. See section II.B.4 Data collection and review of customer expectations, needs, requirements, and specifications)*

25. *Quality information equipment:*

    a. is used only by the Quality Control function.

    b. is used only for the purpose of accepting or rejecting product.

    c. makes measurements of either products or processes and feeds the resulting data back for decision making.

    d. includes automatic electronic instruments but not go/no-go gages.

    *(Answer: **c**. See section II.C Quality information systems)*

26. *In today's world, quality information documentation is called:*

    a. end-item narrative.

    b. hardware.

    c. data pack.

    d. software.

    e. warrantee.

    *(Answer: **d**. See section II.C Quality information systems)*

27. The quality needs for historical information in the areas of specifications, performance reporting, complaint analysis, or run records would fall into which of the following computer application categories?
    a. data accumulation.
    b. data reduction analysis and reporting.
    c. real-time process control.
    d. statistical analysis.
    e. information retrieval.
    (Answer: e. See section II.C Quality information systems)

28. In establishing a quality reporting and information feedback system primary consideration must be given to:
    a. number of inspection stations.
    b. management approval.
    c. timely feedback and corrective action.
    d. historical preservation of data.
    e. routing copy list.
    (Answer: c. See section II.C Quality information systems)

29. All quality information reports should be audited periodically to:
    a. determine their continued validity.
    b. reappraise the routing or copy list.
    c. determine their current effectiveness.
    d. all of the above.
    e. none of the above.
    (Answer: d. See section II.C Quality information systems)

30. When installing a new system for collecting failure data in a manufacturing plant, the following approach is recommended:
    a. issue a procedure written by a quality engineer without help from other departments to prevent a biased input from production test technicians.
    b. have production write their own procedure.

c. *use a procedure from another company.*

d. *enlist the collaboration of all affected departments in drafting and approving the procedure.*

e. *none of the above.*

(Answer: d. See section II.C Quality information systems)

31. *The basic steps in any data processing system using computers generally are arranged in which of the following orders:*
    a. *data input, storage and retrieval, processing and output.*
    b. *collection, analysis, input and output.*
    c. *evaluation, keypunch, processing and output.*
    d. *recording, input, calculation and output.*
    e. *keypunch, FORTRAN programming, output.*
    (Answer: a. See section II.C Quality information systems)

32. *When planning a system for processing quality data or for keeping inspection and other quality records, the first step should be to:*
    a. *depict the system in a flow chart.*
    b. *hire a statistician.*
    c. *investigate applicable data processing equipment.*
    d. *determine the cost of operating the system.*
    e. *start coding your input data.*
    (Answer: a. See section II.C Quality information systems)

33. *The management team is establishing priorities to attack a serious quality problem. You are requested to establish a data collection system to direct this attack. You use which of these general management rules to support your recommendations as to the quantity of data required:*
    a. *you have compared the incremental cost of additional data with the value of the information obtained and stopped when they are equal.*
    b. *your decision corresponds to the rules applicable to management decisions for other factors of production.*

c. your decision is based upon the relationship between value and cost.
d. all of the above.
*(Answer: **d**. See section II.C Quality information systems)*

34. *Computer information processing can become available to a Quality Engineer through the use of:*
  a. a terminal and time sharing agreement.
  b. a batch processing system in which data is brought to a central area for processing.
  c. an in-house system with applicable software.
  d. all of the above.
  *(Answer: **d**. See section II.C Quality information systems)*

35. *Defining the required data output should be:*
  a. performed next after the use of a computer is economically justified.
  b. performed next after input preparation.
  c. done in such a way as to optimize computing formulas.
  d. the first step in computer planning.
  *(Answer: **d**. See section II.C Quality information systems)*

36. *Quality cost trend analysis is facilitated by comparing quality costs to:*
  a. manufacturing costs over the same time period.
  b. appropriate measurement bases.
  c. cash flow reports.
  d. QC department budget.
  *(Answer: **b**. See section II.C Quality information systems)*

37. *The term "random access" identifies information stored:*
  a. where all parts of it are designed to be equally accessible when needed.
  b. someplace inside a computer, whose address only the computer's scanning device can locate.

c. outside a computer, so it has to be sought by humans rather than electronically.

d. in the special part of the processing unit for temporary storage only.

(Answer: a. See section II.C Quality information systems)

38. *An important aid to the quality supervisor in the area of record keeping and data processing is:*

 a. adaptability of records to computer processing.

 b. using well-designed forms and records.

 c. getting sufficient copies of records and reports distributed to key personnel.

 d. training inspectors to follow inspection instructions and procedures.

 (Answer: b. See section II.C Quality information systems)

39. *In planning EDP applications, which element is necessary to reduce computing costs:*

 a. selecting quality control applications having little input and output but extensive calculations.

 b. selecting applications with high volume input and output but simple calculations.

 c. a limited number of highly repetitive jobs.

 d. a group of jobs where output of one determines the input of another.

 (Answer: c. See section II.C Quality information systems)

40. *Management is constantly seeking new ways to make profitable use of their expensive computers. Which of the following computer applications promises to be the most beneficial from management's standpoint?*

 a. decision making help in combination with simulation techniques.

 b. wider use as an accounting machine.

 c. high density information storage and rapid retrieval rates.

 d. solution of complex mathematical formulas.

 (Answer: a. See section II.C Quality information systems)

41. *Source inspection should be employed when:*
    a. *purchasing placed the order late and you want to help.*
    b. *manufacturing is screaming for the material and you want to help.*
    c. *you do not have appropriate gates and management won't buy them.*
    d. *source is more costly than receiving inspection but it reduces backlog in receiving.*
    e. *none of the above.*
    (Answer: c. See section II.D Supplier management)

42. *A vendor quality control plan has been adopted; which of the following provisions would you advise top management to be the least effective?*
    a. *product audits.*
    b. *source inspection.*
    c. *certificate of analysis.*
    d. *certificate of compliance.*
    e. *pre-award surveys.*
    (Answer: d. See section II.D Supplier management)

43. *The most desirable method of evaluating a supplier is:*
    a. *history evaluation.*
    b. *survey evaluation.*
    c. *questionnaire.*
    d. *discuss with quality manager on phone.*
    e. *all of the above.*
    (Answer: a. See section II.D Supplier management)

44. *The most important step in vendor certification is to:*
    a. *obtain copies of vendor's handbook.*
    b. *familiarize vendor with quality requirements.*
    c. *analyze vendor's first shipment.*
    d. *visit the vendor's plant.*
    (Answer: b. See section II.D Supplier management)

45.   When purchasing materials from vendors, it is sometimes advantageous to choose vendors whose prices are higher because:

a. materials which cost more can be expected to be better, and "you get what you pay for."

b. such vendors may become obligated to bestow special favors.

c. such a statement is basically incorrect. Always buy at lowest bid price.

d. the true cost of purchased materials, which should include items such as sorting, inspection, contacting vendors and production delays, may be lower.

(Answer: *d*. See section II.D Supplier management)

46.   Which of the following is not a legitimate audit function?

a. identify function responsible for primary control and corrective action.

b. provide no surprises.

c. provide data on worker performance to supervision for punitive action.

d. contribute to a reduction in quality cost.

e. none of the above.

(Answer: *c*. See section II.E Quality audit)

47.   In many programs, what is generally the weakest link in the quality auditing program?

a. lack of adequate audit check lists.

b. scheduling of audits (frequency).

c. audit reporting.

d. follow-up of corrective action implementation.

(Answer: *d*. See section II.E Quality audit)

48. *What item(s) should be included by management when establishing a quality audit function within their organization?*
    a. *proper positioning of the audit function within the quality organization.*
    b. *a planned audit approach, efficient and timely audit reporting and a method for obtaining effective corrective action.*
    c. *selection of capable audit personnel.*
    d. *management objectivity toward the quality program audit concept.*
    e. *all of the above.*
    (Answer: e. See section II.E Quality audit)

49. *Assurance bears the same relation to the quality function that does to the accounting function:*
    a. *vacation.*
    b. *audit.*
    c. *variable overhead.*
    d. *control.*
    (Answer: b. See section II.E Quality audit)

50. *A pre-award survey of a potential supplier is best described as a _____ audit:*
    a. *compliance*
    b. *assessment*
    c. *quantitative*
    d. *all of these*
    e. *none of these*
    (Answer: b. See section II.E Quality audit)

51. *Which of the following best describes the "specific activity" type of audit?*
    a. *customer oriented sampling of finished goods.*
    b. *evaluation for contractual compliance of quality system.*
    c. *assessment or survey of potential vendor.*

d. an inspection performance audit.

e. none of the above.

(Answer: d. See section II.E Quality audit)

52. *Which of the following techniques would not be used in a quality audit?*
    a. select samples only from completed lots.
    b. examine samples from viewpoint of critical customer.
    c. audit only those items which have caused customer complaints.
    d. use audit information in future design planning.
    e. frequency of audit to depend on economic and quality requirements.
    (Answer: c. See section II.E Quality audit)

53. *During the pre-award survey at a potential key supplier, you discover the existence of a Quality Control Manual, this means:*
    a. that a quality system has been developed.
    b. that a quality system has been implemented.
    c. that the firm is quality conscious.
    d. that the firm has a quality manager.
    e. all of the above.
    (Answer: a. See section II.E Quality audit)

54. *Which of the following quality system provisions is of the* least *concern when preparing an audit check list for the upcoming branch operation quality system audit:*
    a. drawing and print control.
    b. make-up of the MRB (material review board).
    c. engineering design change control.
    d. control of special processes.
    e. calibration of test equipment.
    (Answer: b. See section II.E Quality audit)

55. You are requested by top management to establish an audit program of the quality systems in each branch plant of your firm. Which of the following schemes would you use in selecting the audit team to optimize continuity, direction, availability, and technology transfer?
a. full time audit staff.
b. all volunteer audit staff.
c. the boss' son and son-in-law.
d. hybrid audit staff (a proportion of answers a and b above).
e. any of the above will make an effective audit team
(Answer: d. See section II.E Quality audit)

56. An audit will be viewed as a constructive service to the function which is audited when it:
a. is conducted by non-technical auditors.
b. proposes corrective action for each item uncovered.
c. furnishes enough detailed facts so the necessary action can be determined.
d. is general enough to permit managerial intervention.
(Answer: c. See section II.E Quality audit)

57. Which of the following is not a responsibility of the auditor?
a. prepare a plan and checklist.
b. report results to those responsible.
c. investigate deficiencies for cause and define the corrective action that must be taken.
d. follow up to see if the corrective action was taken.
e. none of the above.
(Answer: c. See section II.E Quality audit)

58. *To insure success of a quality audit program, the most important activity for a quality supervisor is:*
    a. setting up audit frequency.
    b. maintenance of a checking procedure to see that all required audits are performed.
    c. getting corrective action as a result of audit findings.
    d. checking that the audit procedure is adequate and complete.
    (Answer: c. See section II.E Quality audit)

59. *The sample size for a product quality audit should be:*
    a. based on MIL-STD-105E.
    b. based on the lot size.
    c. a stated percentage of production.
    d. very small.
    (Answer: d. See section II.E Quality audit)

60. *It is generally considered desirable that quality audit reports be:*
    a. stated in terms different from those of the function being audited.
    b. simple but complete.
    c. sent to the general manager in all cases.
    d. quantitative in all cases.
    (Answer: b. See section II.E Quality audit)

61. *When looking for existing sources of internal failure cost data, which of the following is usually the best source available?*
    a. operating budgets.
    b. salesmen's field reports.
    c. labor and material cost documents.
    d. returned material reports.
    e. purchase orders.
    (Answer: c. See section II.F Cost of quality)

62. *Of the following, which are typically appraisal costs?*
    a. *vendor surveys and vendor faults.*
    b. *quality planning and quality reports.*
    c. *drawing control centers and material dispositions.*
    d. *quality audits and final inspection.*
    e. *none of the above.*
    (Answer: d. See section II.F Cost of quality)

63. *Which of the following cost elements is normally a prevention cost?*
    a. *receiving inspection.*
    b. *outside endorsements or approvals.*
    c. *design of quality measurement equipment.*
    d. *all of the above.*
    (Answer: c. See section II.F Cost of quality)

64. *When analyzing quality cost data gathered during the initial stages of a new management emphasis on quality control and corrective action as part of a product improvement program, one normally expects to see:*
    a. *increased prevention costs and decreased appraisal costs.*
    b. *increased appraisal costs with little change in prevention costs.*
    c. *decreased internal failure costs.*
    d. *decreased total quality costs.*
    e. *all of these.*
    (Answer: b. See section II.F Cost of quality)

65. *Quality costs are best classified as:*
    a. *cost of inspection and test, cost of quality engineering, cost of quality administration and cost of quality equipment.*
    b. *direct indirect and overhead.*
    c. *cost of prevention, cost of appraisal and cost of failure.*
    d. *unnecessary.*
    e. *none of the above.*
    (Answer: c. See section II.F Cost of quality)

66. *Which of the following bases of performance measurement (denominators), when related to operating quality costs (numerator), would provide reliable indicator(s) to quality management for overall evaluation of the effectiveness of the company's quality program? Quality costs per:*
   a. *total manufacturing costs.*
   b. *unit produced.*
   c. *total direct labor dollars.*
   d. *only one of the above.*
   e. *any two of the above.*
   (Answer: e. See section II.F Cost of quality)

67. *Quality cost data:*
   a. *must be maintained when the end product is for the government.*
   b. *must be mailed to the contracting officer on request.*
   c. *is often an effective means of identifying quality problem areas.*
   d. *all of the above.*
   (Answer: c. See section II.F Cost of quality)

68. *Operating quality costs can be related to different volume bases. An example of volume base that could be used would be:*
   a. *direct labor cost.*
   b. *standard manufacturing cost.*
   c. *processing cost.*
   d. *sales.*
   e. *all of the above.*
   (Answer: e. See section II.F Cost of quality)

69. *When operating a quality cost system, excessive costs can be identified when:*
   a. *appraisal costs exceed failure costs.*
   b. *total quality costs exceed 10% of sales.*
   c. *appraisal and failure costs are equal.*

d. total quality costs exceed 4% of manufacturing costs.

e. there is no fixed rule-management experience must be used.

(Answer: e. See section II.F Cost of quality)

70. Quality cost systems provide for defect prevention. Which of the following elements is primary to defect prevention?

a. corrective action.

b. data collection.

c. cost analysis.

d. training.

(Answer: a. See section II.F Cost of quality)

71. Quality cost analysis has shown that appraisal costs are apparently too high in relation to sales. Which of the following actions probably would not be considered in pursuing this problem?

a. work sampling in inspection and test areas.

b. adding inspectors to reduce scrap costs.

c. pareto analysis of quality costs.

d. considering elimination of some test operations.

e. comparing appraisal costs to bases other than sales—for example direct labor, value added, etc.

(Answer: b. See section II.F Cost of quality)

72. Analyze the cost data below:

$10,000   —equipment design

150,000   —scrap

180,000   —reinspection and retest

45,000   —loss or disposition of surplus stock

4,000   —vendor quality surveys

40,000   —repair

Considering only the Quality Costs shown above, we might conclude that:

a. prevention costs should be decreased.

b. internal failure costs can be decreased.

c. prevention costs are too low a proportion of the quality costs shown.

d. appraisal costs should be increased.

e. nothing can be concluded.

(Answer: c. See section II.F Cost of quality)

73. *This month's quality cost data collection shows the following:*

Returned material processing	*$ 1,800*
Adjustment of customer complaints	*4,500*
Rework and repair	*10,700*
Quality management salaries	*25,000*
Warranty replacement	*54,500*
Calibration and maintenance of test equip	*2,500*
Inspection and testing	*28,000*

For your 'action' report to top management you select which one of the following as the percentage of "External Failure" to "Total Quality Costs" to show the true impact of field problems?

a. 20%

b. 55%

c. 48%

d. 24%

e. 8%

(Answer: c. See section II.F Cost of quality)

74. *You have been assigned as a quality engineer to a small company. The quality control manager desires some cost data and the accounting department reported that the following information is available. Cost accounts are production inspection, $14,185; test inspection, $4,264; procurement inspection, $2,198; shop labor $141,698; shop rework*

$1,402; first article, $675; engineering analysis (rework), $845; repair service (warrantee), $298; quality engineering, $2,175; design engineering salaries, $241,451; quality equipment, $18,745; training, $275; receiving laboratories, $385; underwriters laboratories, $1,200; installation service cost, $9,000: scrap, $1,182; and calibration service, $794.

What are the preventive costs?
a. $3,727
b. $23,701
c. $23,026
d. $3,295
e. $2,450
(Answer: e. See section II.F Cost of quality)

75. *Quality cost analysis has shown that appraisal costs are apparently too high in relation to sales. Which of the following actions probably would not be considered in pursuing this problem?*
a. work sampling in inspection and test areas.
b. adding inspectors to reduce scrap costs.
c. pareto analysis of quality costs.
d. considering elimination of some test operations.
e. comparing appraisal costs to bases other than sales—for example direct labor, value added etc.
(Answer: b. See section II.F Cost of quality)

76. *The percentages of total quality cost are distributed as follows:*

Prevention	*12%*
Appraisal	*28%*
Internal Failure	*40%*
External Failure	*20%*

We conclude:
a. We should invest more money in Prevention.
b. Expenditures for Failures are excessive.
c. The amount spent for Appraisal seems about right.
d. Nothing.
(Answer: d. See section II.F Cost of quality)

77. *One of the following is* not *a factor to consider in establishing quality information equipment cost:*
    a. debugging cost.
    b. amortization period.
    c. design cost.
    d. replacement parts and spares.
    e. book cost.
    (Answer: e. See section II.F Cost of quality)

78. *One method to control inspection costs even without a budget is by comparing _____ as a ratio to productive machine time to produce the product.*
    a. product cost
    b. company profit
    c. inspection hours
    d. scrap material
    (Answer: c. See section II.F Cost of quality)

79. *A complete Quality Cost Reporting System would include which of the following as part of the quality cost?*
    a. test time costs associated with installing the product at the customer's facility prior to turning the product over to the customer.
    b. the salary of a product designer preparing a deviation authorization for material produced outside of design specifications.
    c. cost of scrap.

d. all of the above.

e. none of the above.

(Answer: **d**. See section II.F Cost of quality)

80. When prevention costs are increased to pay for the right kind of engineering work in quality control, a reduction in the number of product defects occurs. This defect reduction means a substantial reduction in _____ .

a. appraisal costs

b. operating costs

c. prevention costs

d. failure costs

e. manufacturing costs

(Answer: **d**. See section II.F Cost of quality)

81. The quality cost of writing instructions and operating procedures for inspection and testing should be charged to:

a. appraisal costs.

b. internal failure costs.

c. prevention costs.

d. external failure costs.

(Answer: **c**. See section II.F Cost of quality)

82. When analyzing quality costs, a helpful method for singling out the highest cost contributors is:

a. a series of interviews with the line foreman.

b. the application of the Pareto theory.

c. an audit of budget variances.

d. the application of break-even and profit volume analysis.

(Answer: **b**. See section II.F Cost of quality)

83. *Included as a "prevention quality cost" would be:*
    a. *salaries of personnel engaged in the design of measurement and control equipment that is to be purchased.*
    b. *capital equipment purchased.*
    c. *training costs of instructing plant personnel to achieve production standards.*
    d. *sorting of nonconforming material which will delay or stop production.*
    (Answer: a. See section II.F Cost of quality)

84. *The modern concept of budgeting quality costs is to:*
    a. *budget each of the four segments: prevention, appraisal, internal and external failure.*
    b. *concentrate on external failures; they are important to the business since they represent customer acceptance.*
    c. *establish budget for reducing the total of the quality costs.*
    d. *reduce expenditures on each segment.*
    (Answer: c. See section II.F Cost of quality)

85. *The percentages of total quality cost are distributed as follows:*

Prevention	*2%*
Appraisal	*33%*
Internal Failure	*35%*
External Failure	*30%*

    We can conclude:
    a. *expenditures for failures are excessive.*
    b. *nothing.*
    c. *we should invest more money in prevention.*
    d. *the amount spent for appraisal seems about right.*
    (Answer: b. See section II.F Cost of quality)

86. *Assume that the cost data available to you for a certain period are limited to the following:*

$ 20,000   —*Final test*
350,000   —*Field warranty costs*
170,000   —*Reinspection and retest*
45,000   —*Loss on disposition of surplus stock*
4,000   —*Vendor quality surveys*
30,000   —*Rework*

The total of the **quality** *costs is:*
a. *$619,000*
b. *$574,000*
c. *$615,000*
d. *$570,000*
*(Answer: **b**. See section II.F Cost of quality)*

87. *In the previous problem the total failure cost is:*
a *$550.000*
b. *$30,000*
c. *$350,000*
d. *$380,000*
*(Answer: **a**. See section II.F Cost of quality)*

88. *In analyzing the cost data in question 74(<depends on previous) we can conclude that:*
a. *prevention cost is too low a proportion of total quality cost.*
b. *total of the quality costs is excessive.*
c. *internal failure costs can be decreased.*
d *appraisal costs should be increased.*
*(Answer: **a**. See section II.F Cost of quality)*

89. *A goal of quality cost report should be to:*
     a. get the best product quality possible.
     b. be able to satisfy MIL-Q-9858A.
     c. integrate two financial reporting techniques.
     d. indicate areas of excessive costs.
     (Answer: d. See section II.F Cost of quality)

90. *The concept of quality cost budgeting:*
     a. involves budgeting the individual elements.
     b. replaces the traditional profit and loss statement.
     c. does not consider total quality costs.
     d. considers the four categories of quality costs and their general trends.
     (Answer: d. See section II.F Cost of quality)

91. *Sources of quality cost data do not normally include:*
     a. scrap reports.
     b. labor reports.
     c. salary budget reports.
     d. capital expenditure reports.
     (Answer: d. See section II.F Cost of quality)

92. *When one first analyzes quality cost data, he might expect to find that,*
     relative to total quality costs:
     a. costs of prevention are high.
     b. costs of appraisal are high.
     c. costs of failure are high.
     d. all of above.
     (Answer: c. See section II.F Cost of quality)

93. Quality costs should not be reported against which one of following measurement bases:
   a. direct labor.
   b. sales.
   c. net profit.
   d. unit volume of production.
   (Answer: c. See section II.F Cost of quality)

94. The basic objective of a quality cost program is to:
   a. identify the source of quality failures.
   b. determine quality control department responsibilities.
   c. utilize accounting department reports.
   d. improve the profit posture of your company.
   (Answer: d. See section II.F Cost of quality)

95. The distribution of a characteristic is negatively skewed. The sampling distribution of the mean for large samples is:
   a. negatively skewed.
   b. approximately normal.
   c. positively skewed.
   d. bimodal.
   e. Poisson.
   (Answer: b. See section II.G Continuous improvement tools)

96. If a process is out of control, the theoretical probability that four consecutive points on an X chart will fail on the same side of the mean is:
   a. unknown.
   b $(1/2)4$
   c $2 \cdot (1/2)4$
   d $1/2 \cdot (1/2)4$
   (Answer: a. See section II.G Continuous improvement tools)

97. *A useful tool to determine when to investigate excessive variation in a process is*
    a. MIL-STD-105E.
    b. control chart.
    c. Dodge-Romig AOQL sampling table.
    d. process capability study.
    (Answer: b. See section II.G.1 Quality tools)

98. *Shewhart $\overline{X}$ control charts are designed with which one of the following objectives?*
    a. reduce sample size.
    b. fix risk of accepting poor product.
    c. decide when to hunt for causes of variation.
    d. establish an acceptable quality level.
    (Answer: c. See section II.G.1 Quality tools)

99. *The most important reason for a checklist in a process control audit is to:*
    a. assure that the auditor is qualified.
    b. minimize the time required for audit.
    c. obtain relatively uniform audits.
    d. notify the audited function prior to audit.
    (Answer: c. See section II.G.1 Quality tools)

100. *Let X be any random variable with mean μ and standard deviation σ. Take a random sample of size n. As n increases and as a result of the Central Limit Theorem:*
    a. The distribution of the sum $S_n = X_1 + X_2 + \ldots + X_n$ approaches a normal distribution with mean μ and standard deviation $\sigma/\sqrt{n}$
    b. The distribution of $S_n = X_1 + X_2 + \ldots + X_n$ approaches a normal distribution with mean m and standard deviation $\sigma/\sqrt{n}$

c. *The distribution of X approaches a normal distribution with mean $n \mu$ and standard deviation $\sigma / \sqrt{n}$*

d. *None of the above.*

*(Answer: **d**. See section II.G.1 Quality tools)*

CHAPTER

III

Statistical Principles and Applications

A. SOLUTIONS TO SELECTED EXERCISES FOUND IN *THE COMPLETE GUIDE TO THE CQE*

1. *Classify the following as belong to either enumerative or analytic statistical studies:*
   a. *clinical trial of a new drug.*
   b. *changes in the Dow Jones industrial average.*
   c. *changes in the unemployment rate.*
   d. *changes in the rate of inflation.*
   e. *epidemeologic study of the link between smoking and lung cancer.*
   f. *designed experiment to evaluate a new tool.*
      Enumerative: *a, f.* Analytic: *b, c, d, e.*
   (See section III.A Terms and concepts)

2. *Critique the following statement: "The X-bar chart shows statistical control. Therefore, we can state that the probability that the next subgroup mean will be within the control limits is 99.73%."*
   The control chart is an analytic tool. The statement treats it as if it were an enumerative statistical technique. The statement applies to the future, which cannot be predicted with such extreme precision. The

best one can do would be something like "If the process remains stable, there is only a small chance of a subgroup mean beyond the control limits."
(See section III.A Terms and concepts)

3. *Identify the scales of measurement for the following:*
   a. diameter of a hole
   b. customer complaint
   c. customer response on a scale of 1 (strongly agree) to 5 (strongly disagree)
   d. true position location of a part feature
   e. pH of a chemical solution
      a = ratio scale
      b = nominal scale
      c = ordinal scale
      d = ratio scale
      e = interval scale
   (See section III.A Terms and concepts)

4. *Two stable processes have the same means. However, process A has a larger variance than process B. Which is the better process and why?*
   Process B is better. Taguchi showed that, other things being equal, smaller variance produces smaller total cost.
   (See section III.A Terms and concepts)

5. *Obtain a newspaper with a classified section and create a stem-and-leaf plot of the asking prices of 20 automobiles, selected at random.*
   (See section III.A Terms and concepts)

6. *Sketch a boxplot of the following statistics:*

Smallest = 60	*25th percentile = 80*
Median = 100	*75th percentile = 110*
Largest = 115	

   There are no outliers. Comment on the shape of this distribution.

   The distribution is skewed to the left, or skewed low.

   (See section III.A Terms and concepts)

7. *Compare the two conceptual frameworks for addressing premises questions in statistical inference.*

   (See section III.A.5 Inferential statistics)

8. *Machine A produces 20% of all of the parts and its output is 1% defective. An item is selected at random from the warehouse:*

   a. *what is the probability that the item is a defective produced by machine A?*

   b. *if machine A accounts for 50% of all defectives produced, what is the probability that the item is either defective or produced by machine A?*

   a. P(machine A $\cap$ defective) = P(machine A) * P(defective from A)
      = 0.2 * 0.01 = 0.002

   b. P(machine A $\cup$ defective) = P(machine A) + P(defective)
      − P(machine A $\cap$ defective) = 0.2+0.02 − 0.002 = 0.218

   (See section III.C Statistical inference)

9. *Three coins are flipped. How many outcomes are possible?*

   2^3 = 8

   (See section III.C Statistical inference)

10. *Find 5!*

    5*4*3*2*1 = 120

    (See section III.C Statistical inference)

11. *How many combinations can be made from a sample of 5 items with 2 defective items?*
    (See section III.C Statistical inference)

12. *Demonstrate the central limit theorem as follows: take 20 coins, shake them and drop them. Count the number of heads. Repeat the process 50 times. Plot a histogram of the number of heads. The shape of the histogram will be approximately normal.*
    (See section III.C Statistical inference)

13. *Determine the expected gain or loss for 50 bets of $1 each on a roulette wheel. You are betting on black. The wheel has 18 red slots, 18 black slots and 2 green slots.*

$$E[gain] = +\$50\left(\frac{18}{38}\right) - \$50\left(\frac{20}{38}\right) = -\$2.63$$

i.e., on average you will lose $2.63 for every $50 bet.
(See section III.C Statistical inference)

14. *A stable process has a distribution with mean = 100, median = 90. Comment on the shape of this distribution.*

    Since the mean and median are not equal, the distribution is not symmetric. Since the mean is greater than the median, the distribution is skewed right.
    (See section III.B Distributions)

15. *A stable process has a distribution with mean = 100, median = 110. Comment on the shape of this distribution.*

    Since the mean and median are not equal, the distribution is not symmetric. Since the mean is less than the median, the distribution is skewed left.
    (See section III.B Distributions)

16. *Draw the cumulative frequency ogive of the following frequency table:*

SIZE (mm)	25.0	25.1	25.2	25.3	25.4	25.5	25.6	25.7	25.8
FREQUENCY	30	45	100	90	60	55	45	30	10

Cumulative frequency ogive created from the above data.

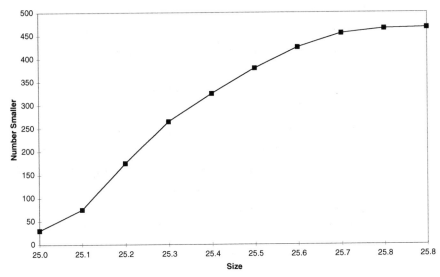

(See section III.B Distributions)

17. *A stable process has a standard deviation of 100. What is the standard deviation of averages of samples of n = 25 from this process?*

$$S_{\bar{X}} = \frac{S}{\sqrt{n}} = \frac{100}{5} = 20$$

(See section III.B Distributions)

18. *The technician computed the population standard deviation to be 100. However, the data were actually a sample of n = 10. What is the sample standard deviation?*

The population standard deviation is a biased estimator when used with sample data (see the discussion of Equation III.12 on page 241 of

The Complete Guide to the CQE). The sample standard deviation is found as follows:

$$s = \sqrt{\frac{n}{n-1}}\sigma = \sqrt{\frac{10}{9}} \times 100 = 105.41$$

(See section III.B Distributions)

19. **Compute the mean and standard deviation of the following sample data: 15, 21, 18, 11, 7.**
    Mean = 14.4, sigma = 5.55 (rounded).
    (See section III.B Distributions)

20. **Using the binomial distribution find the probability that a sample of n = 10 from a process with proportion defective p=0.1 will have exactly 1 defective item. Less than 2 defectives?**
    $P(x=1) = 0.39$.
    $P(x<2) = 1 - P(x=0) - P(x=1) = 1 - 0.35 - 0.39 = 0.26$
    (See section III.B Distributions)

21. **Repeat the above problem using the Poisson approximation to the binomial. Note: the recommended conditions are not met in this example, however, it remains a useful exercise.**
    $np = 10 * 0.1 = 1$
    $P(x=1) = 0.37$
    $P(x<2) = 1 - P(x=0) - P(x=1) = 1 - 0.37 - 0.37 = 0.26$
    (See section III.B Distributions)

22. **A busy intersection averages three accidents per week. Using the Poisson distribution estimate the probability that there will be one or more accidents in the next 24 hours.**
    Mean = 3/7 accidents-per-day
    $P(x>0) = 1.0 - P(x=0) = 1.0 - 0.65 = 0.35$
    (See section III.B Distributions)

23.   *A delivery of 20 items was made to your receiving dock from a warehouse. The inspector suggests taking a random sample of 10 items and accepting the lot if no defectives are found. Use the hypergeometric distribution to determine the probability of accepting the lot with this sampling plan if there are actually 3 defectives in the lot.*

    0.1053

(See section III.B Distributions)

24.   *Compute the population mean, variance and standard deviation for the following two populations:*

    Population #1: 4, 5, 6, 7, 8   *Population #2: 2, 4, 6, 8, 10*

	POPULATION #1	POPULATION #2
MEAN	6	6
VARIANCE	2	8
STANDARD DEVIATION	1.414	2.828

(See section III.B Distributions)

25.   *A stable milling process has a mean of 100mm and a standard deviation of 5mm.*

    a. Compute the Z transformation for the lower specification of 92mm.

    b. Assuming the process has a normal distribution, estimate the percentage of items that will be undersize.

    a. $Z = -1.6$.

    b. Estimated percent undersize = 5.48%.

(See section III.B Distributions)

26. *A machine with a stable control chart produces holes with a mean size of 0.501 inches and standard deviation of 0.0015 inches. The engineering requirement is for holes between 0.497 inches and 0.503 inches. Assuming a normal distribution, what percentage of these parts will meet the requirements?*

    Low specification: Z = –2.67, undersize = 0.38%.

    High specification: Z = 1.33, oversize = 9.18%.

    Meets requirements: 90.44%.

(See section III.B Distributions)

27. *At a busy intersection accidents occur, on average, once every 3 days. What is the probability that an accident will occur in the next 24 hours? (Use the exponential distribution).*

    0.2835

(See section III.B Distributions)

28. *The standard deviation of a stable process is 0.025mm. What is the probability that a sample of n = 10 will have a standard deviation of 0.05mm or greater? (Use the χ^2 distribution.)*

$$\chi^2 = \frac{(n-1)s^2}{\sigma^2} = \frac{9(0.05^2)}{0.025^2} = 36$$

    Referring to Appendix Table 7 for 9 degrees of freedom we see that this value falls beyond the 0.001 point in the tail, which is 27.877.

(See section III.B Distributions)

29. *Use the t distribution to compute a 90% confidence interval for μ. The mean of a sample of n=9 is 16. Assume that σ is known to be 4. Describe the confidence interval in words.*

    $13.8067 < \mu < 18.1933$.

    This means that, if the assumptions are met, there is a 90% probability that the true mean lies between 13.8067 and 18.1933.

(See section III.B Distributions)

30. *Use the t distribution to compute a 90% confidence interval for μ. The mean of a sample of n=9 is 16. Assume that σ is not known but was computed to be 4 based on the sample. Describe the confidence interval in words.*

   $13.52 < \mu < 18.48$. This means that, if the assumptions are met, there is a 90% probability that the true mean lies between 13.52 and 18.48. *(See section III.B Distributions)*

31. *The process engineer believes that a modified process will produce the same results as the existing process, while costing less. The existing process was stable with a mean of 50mm. The process engineer ran 25 units with the new process. The control chart for the 25 units was stable, the sample mean was 49 and the standard deviation was 0.5. Are these results consistent with the process engineer's original premise?*
   a. Set up a formal test of hypothesis for this problem, including the critical region.
   b. Conduct the hypothesis test at a 5% level of significance.
   a. H_0: μ=50mm, H_1: $\mu \neq$50mm, α=0.05, $-2.064 \leq t_0 \leq 2.064$.

   b. $t = \dfrac{\mu - \overline{X}}{s / \sqrt{n}} = \dfrac{50 - 49}{0.5 / \sqrt{25}} = 10$ which is well outside of the
   critical region. Thus, we reject the null hypothesis and conclude that the mean of the modified process is no longer 50mm.
   (See section III.B Distributions)

32. *Two gages are used to inspect an item, yours and your supplier's. A correlation sample of n=25 units was inspected using both gages. The standard deviation using gage #1 is 20, using gage #2 it is 30. Are these variances significantly different at a 5% level of significance?*

$$F = \frac{30^2}{20^2} = 2.25$$

The critical value of $F_{0.95, 24, 24} = 1.98$. Thus, we conclude that the variances are significantly different. See Appendix Table 9.
(See section III.B Distributions)

33. *Given the linear equation y = 150 + 35x.*
    a. *What is the intercept?*
    b. *What is the slope?*
    c. *When x=2, what is y?*
    d. *What is y when x=0?*
    e. *If the target for y is 200, what value should x be?*
    f. *How much will y change if x changes by one unit?*
        a. 150
        b. 35
        c. 220
        d. 150
        e. 1.4286
        f. 35
    (See section III.D Correlation and regression analysis)

34. *Using a computer, perform a least-squares regression of analysis of the data below, let x=caliper reading, y=micrometer reading:*

	1	2	3	4	5	6	7	8	9	10
Micrometer	105	107	110	115	117	119	123	125	128	130
Caliper	103	106	108	114	115	117	121	124	126	129

SUMMARY OUTPUT					
Regression statistics					
Multiple R	0.998				
R Square	0.997				
Adjusted R Square	0.996				
Standard Error	0.538				
Observations	10.000				
ANOVA					
	df	*ss*	*ms*	*F*	*Significance F*
Regression	1.000	680.587	680.587	2354.364	0.000
Residual	8.000	2.313	0.289		
Total	9.000	682.900			
	Coefficients	*Standard error*	*t Stat*	*P-value*	
Intercept	2.903	2.376	1.222	0.257	
Caliper	0.989	0.020	48.522	0.000	

(See section III.D Correlation and regression analysis)

35. Write the linear regression equation for the above example.
   Micrometer reading = 2.903 + 0.989 * (caliper reading)
   (See section III.D Correlation and regression analysis)

36. The engineer wants to estimate the micrometer reading that would result from a caliper reading of 150. Comment on this prediction.
   The data space does not include 150, thus the engineer is extrapolating. Extrapolation should be avoided whenever possible. The engineer should extend the data space to cover the entire range of concern. If he must extrapolate to 150, he should at least verify his extrapolation for that single value.
   (See section III.D Correlation and regression analysis)

37. *"The standard error is 1.5." Describe the meaning of this phrase with respect to a regression analysis, assuming the model is valid.*

For a model which fits the data, the standard error represents the standard deviation of the residuals. The error distribution is normal with a mean of zero. Thus, the above phrase means that the distribution of the residuals is normal with a mean of zero and a standard deviation of 1.5.

(See section III.D Correlation and regression analysis)

38. *The slope of the regression equation is 10. The average of the X's is 25 and the average of the Y's is 50. Find the intercept of the linear model.*

Using Equation III.30 (page 278 in *The Complete Guide to the CQE*) the intercept is computed as $a = 50 - 10*25 = -200$.

(See section III.D Correlation and regression analysis)

39. *Describe R^2 in words.*

R^2 is also called the coefficient of determination or the coefficient of multiple determination. It is the square of the correlation coefficient so it is always positive. It tells the proportion of the total variation about the mean Y-bar, explained by the regression.

(See section III.D Correlation and regression analysis)

40. *The regression ANOVA table has a p-value of 0.01. Interpret this result.*

The ANOVA table for a regression tests the hypothesis that the variation explained by the regression model is actually zero. The result means that the probability that the hypothesis is true is very small, about 1%. This does **not** mean that the regression model describes an actual cause-and-effect relationship. Explaining the precise nature of the relationships among variables is a matter of subject matter expertise, not statistics.

(See section III.D Correlation and regression analysis)

41. **Explain the difference between correlation analysis and regression analysis.**

    (See section III.D Correlation and regression analysis)

42. **Using a run chart, analyze the following data:**

DATE	ORDERS SHIPPED	DATE	ORDERS SHIPPED
Jan-94	360	Oct-94	375
Feb-94	342	Nov-94	346
Mar-94	399	Dec-94	384
Apr-94	378	Jan-95	332
May-94	376	Feb-95	343
Jun-94	378	Mar-95	341
Jul-94	358	Apr-95	302
Aug-94	410	May-95	327
Sep-94	418	Jun-95	329

   The analysis should include drawing a run chart with the median shown and analyzing run length, number of runs and trend analysis.
   (See section III.D Correlation and regression analysis)

43. **Compute the Durbin-Watson statistic using the data below (taken from the previous exercise.) Is there evidence of serial correlation?**

Observation	Predicted Y	Residuals
1	392.228	-32.228
2	388.299	-46.299
3	384.370	14.630
4	380.442	-2.442
5	376.513	-0.513
6	372.584	5.416
7	368.655	-10.655
8	364.727	45.273

Continued on next page . . .

Continued from previous page . . .

Observation	Predicted Y	Residuals
9	360.798	57.202
10	356.869	18.131
11	352.940	-6.940
12	349.011	34.989
13	345.083	-13.083
14	341.154	1.846
15	337.225	3.775
16	333.296	-31.296
17	329.367	-2.367
18	325.439	-35.439

Solution (note: the student's answer may differ slightly due to round off):

Observation	Predicted Y	Residuals	Col C squared	Lag ^{2}
1	392.228	-32.228	1038.649	
2	388.299	-46.299	2143.623	197.999
3	384.370	14.630	214.023	3712.318
4	380.442	-2.442	5.962	291.426
5	376.513	-0.513	0.263	3.720
6	372.584	5.416	29.332	35.151
7	368.655	-10.655	113.536	258.284
8	364.727	45.273	2049.688	3128.030
9	360.798	57.202	3272.100	142.296
10	356.869	18.131	328.735	1526.559
11	352.940	-6.940	48.166	628.565
12	349.011	34.989	1224.205	1758.024
13	345.083	-13.083	171.153	2310.841
14	341.154	1.846	3.409	222.869

Continued on next page . . .

Continued from previous page . . .

Observation	Predicted Y	Residuals	Col C squared	Lag ^2
15	337.225	3.775	14.251	3.720
16	333.296	-31.296	979.451	1229.990
17	329.367	-2.367	5.605	836.875
18	325.439	-35.439	1255.894	1093.705
		TOTALS	12898.043	17380.371
Durbin-Watson	1.348			

Table 12 in the Appendix gives the lower and upper bounds on D as d_L=1.16, d_U=1.39. Based on these values we cannot reach a conclusion regarding serial correlation, more data is needed.
(See section III.D Correlation and regression analysis)

44. *An experiment is proposed to determine the ability of different human subjects to reproduce lines freehand. The experimenter wants to know the effect of viewing distance (long or short) and reference line length (short or long). Subjects will be shown two lines of length known only to the investigator (not known to the subjects) and asked to draw a line of the length shown without using any mechanical aids or measuring the reference line in any way other than simply looking at it. Prepare a plan for this experiment.*

The plan must answer a number of questions. What is the short/long line length and distance to be? How many subjects are to be used? How will subjects be selected to assure external validity? Are interactions important? How will the experimental units be created (i.e., the objects with the lines drawn on them)? How will subject-to-subject variation be handled (e.g., different vision ability)? How will randomization be assured? How many replications are to be performed? Is blocking necessary? How will background variables be handled? etc.

The instructor may wish to create a checklist of the above items plus any others he can think of and grade the students based on items omitted, giving extra credit for other important items included. An interesting educational exercise is to compare the various student responses to one another.

(See section III.E Experimental design)

45. **Conduct the above experiment using two subjects and 1 replicate. Analyze the results using the Yates method. Prepare an experimental report.**

    The report should discuss the main effects, two- and- three-factor interactions and conclusions of the student. The conclusions should involve the magnitude and significance of the observed effects and the applicability of the results to subjects beyond the experiment (e.g., based on only two subjects the results cannot be generalized to the entire human race, but how broadly applicable are they?).

    (See section III.E Experimental design)

46. **The experiment described above was conducted (correctly, of course!) and the following results obtained:**

		Length of Line			
		Short		Long	
Viewing Distance →		Near	Far	Near	Far
Subject 1	Trial 1	1	7	2	9
	Trial 2	0	5	3	7
Subject 2	Trial 1	3	6	2	10
	Trial 2	1	6	2	12

   The data in the table are the differences, in mm, between the reference line and the freehand line. Analyze the data using the Yates method.
   (See section III.E Experimental design)

47. **What are the three major aspects of off-line quality control?**
    System design, parameter design and tolerance design.
    (See section III.E Experimental design)

48. *Explain the difference between the Taguchi loss model and the traditional "goal-post" loss model.*
    (See section III.E Experimental design)

49. *Some cars are sold to people who live in Detroit, others to people who live in Arizona, and still others to people who drive regularly between cities in the North and the South. What is the Taguchi term that describes this variation?*
    External noise.
    (See section III.E Experimental design)

50. *The zinc plating on parts of the car's underbody varies in thickness. What is the Taguchi term that describes this variation?*
    Internal noise.
    (See section III.E Experimental design)

51. *An experiment was conducted and the results obtained. The experimenter predicted that optimum performance would occur from an acceptable process setting that was outside the data space. The recommended setting was written into the process plan at once. Is this an example of the Taguchi method? If not, why not?*
    No. Even if all other steps were followed (and there is nothing in the exercise description that tells you one way or the other), the confirmation step was not done. Taguchi experiments produce mathematical models that are often used to find theoretically optimal process settings. Taguchi experiments usually create what are known as "sparse matrices." This means that many of the experimental conditions were not actually tried. The confirmation step is extremely important for this type of experiment; many statisticians recommend even more experimental proof before concluding the optimum has been found, e.g., another set of experiments in the neighborhood of the predicted optimum.
    (See section III.E Experimental design)

52. *A process is in statistical control, should acceptance sampling be used?*

No. Both economic and statistical proofs have been discovered to show that optimal inspection is always at 0% or 100% for stable processes. The engineer should determine the process proportion defective from the control chart and apply Deming's all-or-none rule. *(See section III.F Acceptance sampling)*

53. *A very large lot has been received on the dock. There is no data on the process that created the lot. Should acceptance sampling be used?*

No. The engineer should take a random sample of $n=200$, estimate the lot proportion defective, and apply Deming's all-or-none rule. *(See section III.F Acceptance sampling)*

54. *A small lot of items from an unknown process has arrived on the dock. Should acceptance sampling be used?*

Yes. This author believes that acceptance sampling can be applied in this circumstance. However, this circumstance should be relatively rare. *(See section III.F Acceptance sampling)*

55. *A critical characteristic is to be inspected. Should acceptance sampling be used?*

No. In general, critical characteristics should be subjected to 100% inspection and/or test. *(See section III.F Acceptance sampling)*

56. *Evaluate the single sampling plan* n = *50,* c = *2,* N = *150.*

The evaluation should use the worksheet in Figure III.44 from *The Complete Guide to the CQE.* The OC curve and AOQ curve should be plotted. The AOQL should be computed or estimated from the AOQ curve. *(See section III.F Acceptance sampling)*

57. *An item costs $0.75 to inspect. If the item is defective its lifetime cost will be $50 higher than if it were non-defective. The items are produced by a stable process with an average defective rate of 1%. Should the items be*
   a. *acceptance sampling,*
   b. *100% inspection, or*
   c. *0% inspection?*

   Using Deming's all-or-none rule we compute $0.75/$50.00 = 0.015. Since this value is greater than the average of 0.01, the items will be shipped without additional inspection.
   (See section III.F Acceptance sampling)

58. *What is the main advantage of double sampling plans compared with single sampling plans? The disadvantages (if any?)*

   The principle advantage is that, on average, double sampling plans require fewer samples than single sampling plans with similar operating characteristics. The principal disadvantage is additional administrative and scheduling difficulty.
   (See section III.F Acceptance sampling)

59. *Find the sampling plan in Mil-Std-105E or ANSI/ASQC Z1.9 based on the following criteria: single sample, normal inspection, AQL 1.0%, Lot size* N = *1,000.*
   (See section III.F Acceptance sampling)

B. DETAILED SOLUTIONS TO SELECTED PAST EXAM QUESTIONS

1. *What is the standard deviation of the following sample 3.2, 3.1, 3.3, 3.3, 3.1?*

    a. 3.2

    b. 0.0894

    c. 0.1

    d. 0.0498

    e. 0.2

    The sample standard deviation is given by

$$s = \sqrt{\frac{\sum_{i=1}^{n}(X_i^2) - \overline{X}(\sum_{i=1}^{n} X_i)}{n-1}}$$

For these data

i	Xi	Xi²
1	3.2	10.24
2	3.1	9.61
3	3.3	10.89
4	3.3	10.89
5	3.1	9.61
SUM	16	51.24

$$\overline{X} = \frac{16}{5} = 3.2, \ n = 5$$

$$s = \sqrt{\frac{51.24 - 3.2(16)}{5-1}} = 0.1$$

Choice *c*. Anyone taking the CQE exam should have a pocket calculator that computes $\overline{X}$ and s automatically.

(See section III.A Terms and concepts)

The following mini-case study applies to questions 2, 3 and 4.

Mini-Case Study

A certain equipment manufacturer offers warranty on his product for a period of one year after installation. His investigation revealed the following additional information:

Each of these time lags is normally distributed, and each is independent of the other. (For example, time to failure is independent of equipment age at time of installation.)

In February of last year, this manufacturer produced 4,000 units of a particular model. Through December of the same year (45 weeks), a total of 23 warranty claims had been processed on these 4,000 units.

	MEAN	STD DEVIATION
Time lag from date of production to date of sale (to dealer or distributor)	10 weeks	3 weeks
Time lag from date of sale to date of installation	14 weeks	3.5 weeks
Time lag from date of installation to date of processing warranty claim	30 weeks	10 weeks

Carry all calculations to *three* places.

2. *The standard deviation of total time from date of production to date of processing claims is:*

   a. ten (10) weeks.

   b. eleven (11) weeks.

   c. thirteen and one-half (13.5) weeks.

   d. sixteen and one-half (16.5) weeks.

   The needed statistical relation is

   $$\sigma^2_{sum} = \text{Sum of individual } \sigma^2.$$

For this problem

$$\sigma_{\text{total lag}} = \sqrt{3^2 + 3.5^2 + 10^2} = 11.01 \text{ weeks}$$

Choice *b.*
(See section III.A Terms and concepts)

3. *What proportion of the likely total (eventual) number of warranty claims on February's production has been processed through December?*
   a. 0.186
   b. 0.207
   c. 0.468
   d. 0.532
   e. 0.793

   To answer this we need to know the additional things
   • The mean of the sum = the sum of the means.
   • The sum of independent normally distributed random variables is normally distributed. The mean time between production and processing is

   $$\overline{X}_{\text{total lag}} = 10 + 14 + 30 = 54 \text{ weeks}$$

   There are 45 weeks from the end of February through the end of December. We already know $\sigma_{\text{total lag}}$ from question 62. What we are asked, therefore, is

   "What proportion of a normally distributed variable with a mean = 54 and σ = 11 will be below X = 44?"

   We compute

   $$Z = \frac{X - \overline{X}}{\sigma} = \frac{45 - 54}{11} = -0.82$$

   and enter the normal tables to get
   Proportion = 0.206
   Which is closest to choice *b.*

Proportion of claims processed.

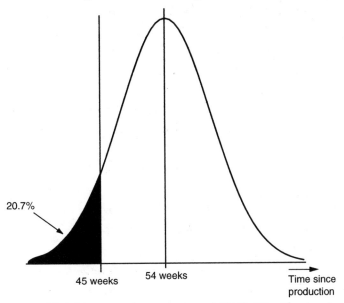

(See section III.A Terms and concepts, and III.B Distributions)

4. *How many of these units are likely to eventually result in warranty claims?*
   a. 28
   b. 55
   c. 88
   d. 111
   e. 152

$$\text{Expected total} = \frac{23}{0.207} = 111 \text{ claims}$$

Since 23 claims have been processed, and this is 20.7% of the expected total

Choice *d.*

(See section III.A Terms and concepts)

5. *A number derived from sample data, which describes the data in some useful way, is called a:*
   a. constant.
   b. statistic.
   c. parameter.
   d. critical value.

   A *statistic* is a value computed from sample *data.* Statistics are often used to make inferences about population *parameters.* The correct answer is *b.*

   (See section III.A Terms and concepts)

6. *For the Normal Probability Distribution, the relationships among the median, mean and mode are that:*
   a. they are all equal to the same value.
   b. the mean and mode have the same value but the median is different.
   c. each has a value different from the other two.
   d. the mean and median are the same but the mode is different.

   The normal distribution is unimodal and symmetric; thus the mean, median, and mode are all the same (answer *a*).

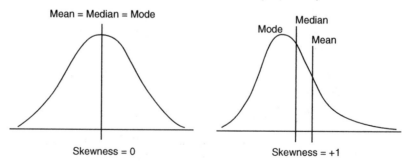

Definitions:
   Mean—Sum of values/Number of values.
   Median—Value that 50% are greater than and 50% are less than.
   Mode—The value that occurs most frequently.
   (See section III.A Terms and concepts)

7. *A sample of n observations has a mean $\overline{X}$ and standard deviation $s_x > 0$. If a single observation, which equals the value of the sample mean $\overline{X}$, is removed from the sample, which of the following is true?*
   a. *$\overline{X}$ and s_x both change.*
   b. *$\overline{X}$ and s_x remain the same.*
   c. *$\overline{X}$ remains the same but s_x increases*
   d. *$\overline{X}$ remains the same but s_x decreases.*

   The two equations of interest are

$$\overline{X} = \frac{1}{n} \sum_{i=1}^{n} x_i$$

and

$$s^2 = \sum_{i=1}^{n} \frac{(x_i - \overline{X})^2}{n-1}$$

Since S>0 we know that Xi $\neq \overline{X}$ for at least one i. If we remove a single observation exactly equal to $\overline{X}$ then the numerator sum in the equation of S will be unchanged (since we are deleting a zero) but the denominator will change from n-l to n-2; thus S will increase. The next task is to show that $\overline{X}$ will be unchanged. Let us define

$$S1 = \sum_{i=1}^{n} X_i \quad \text{and} \quad S2 = S1 - \overline{X}$$

The value of $\overline{X}$ after removing a value exactly equal to $\overline{X}$ will be

$$\overline{X}_2 = S2/(n-1) = \frac{S1 - \overline{X}}{n-1} = \frac{S1 - \frac{S1}{n}}{n-1} = \frac{S1\left(\frac{n-1}{n}\right)}{n-1} = S1/n = \overline{X}$$

The correct answer is *c*.
(*See section III.A Terms and concepts*)

8. *For two events, A and B, one of the following is a true probability statement.*
    a. P(A or B) = P(A) + P(B) if A and B are independent.
    b. P(A or B) = P(A) + P(B) if A and B are mutually exclusive.
    c. P(A and B) = P(A) x P(B) if A and B are mutually exclusive.
    d. P(A and B) = P(A) x P(B) if A and B are independent.
    Choice *b* is correct, as is easily seen from the Venn diagram below

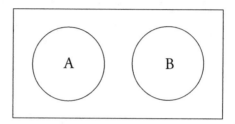

$$P(A \text{ or } B) = P(A) + P(B)$$

Two events A and B are mutually exclusive if they have no common elements. That is, the *intersection* of A and B is an empty set. *(See section III.A Terms and concepts)*

9. *For a certain maker of car, the factory-installed brake linings have a mean lifetime of 40,000 miles with a 5,000 mile standard deviation. A sample of 100 cars has been selected for testing. Assuming that the finite population correction may be ignored, the standard error of $\overline{X}$ is:*
    a. 50 miles.
    b. 500 miles.
    c. 400 miles.
    d. 4,000 miles.
    The standard error of the mean is given by

$$S_{\overline{X}} = \frac{S}{\sqrt{n}}$$

    where S = standard deviation of individuals
        n = the sample size

For this problem S = 5000 and n = 100, thus

$$S_{\bar{x}} = \frac{5000}{\sqrt{100}} = 500$$

Choice *b*. Note: The finite population correction is $\left(1 - \frac{n}{N}\right)$, where N = population, n = sample size.
(See section III.B Distributions)

10. *You have been asked to sample a lot of 300 units from a vendor whose past quality has been about 2% defective. A sample of 40 pieces is drawn from the lot and you have been told to reject the lot if you find two or more parts defective. What is the probability of finding two or more parts defective?*

   a. .953
   b. .809
   c. .191
   d. .047

   The exact probability can be found using the binomial distribution, assuming continuous production. However, the Poisson distribution should give an adequate—and much faster—approximation. We first compute

   $$np = 40 \text{ x } .02 = 0.8$$

   And then recall that

   Prob (2 or more) = 1 − Prob (1 or less)

   This is important because the probability of X *or less* is given by most Poisson tables. Entering Appendix Table 10 we find for n = 0.8, r = 1

   Prob (1 or less) = 0.809

   Thus

   Prob (2 or more) = 1 − 0.809 = 0.191

   Choice *c*.
   (See section III.B Distributions)

11. *What is the probability of finding no defective items in a random sample of 100 items taken from the output of a continuous process which averages 0.7% defective items?*

    a. 0.49

    b. 1.74

    c. 0.10

    d. 0.74

    e. 0.33

    Again, the Poisson should be tried first due to the speed with which one can obtain a result; however, the exact distribution is the binomial. We compute

    $$np = 100 \times .7\% = 100 \times .007 = .7$$

    And entering the Poisson table 10 we find

    $$\text{Prob } (0) = .497$$

    Choice *a* is the only one close.

    (See section III.B Distributions)

12. *A process is producing material which is 30% defective. Five pieces are selected at random for inspection. What is the probability of exactly two good pieces being found in the sample?*

    a. .868

    b. .309

    c. .436

    d. .132

    We will use the binomial distribution to get

    $$P(x) = C_x^n p^x (1-p)^{n-x}$$

    where x = the number of *good pieces*

    n = the sample size

    p = the proportion *good*

$$\text{Prob}(x \text{ equals } 2) = C_2^5 (.7)^2 (1 - .7)^{5-2}$$

$$= \frac{5!}{2!3!} (.49)(.027) = .132$$

Choice *d.*

(See section III.B Distributions)

13. *An inspection plan is set up to randomly sample 3 ft.² of a 1,000 ft.² carpet and to accept the carpet only if no flaws are found in the 3 ft.² sample. What is the probability that a roll of carpet with an average of one (1) flaw per square foot will be rejected by the plan?*

    a. .05

    b. .72

    c. .90

    d. .95

    The correct distribution is the Poisson. The parameter we need to use the table is μ, found as follows:

    Defects per unit = 1

    Units per sample = 3

    μ = (Defects per unit) x (Units per sample) = 3

    The roll will be rejected if we find 1 or more defects in our sample. Thus

    $$\text{Prob (rej)} = 1 - \text{Prob (0 defects)}$$

    Entering the Poisson table with $\mu = 3$ we find

    $$\text{Prob (0)} = .05$$

    Thus

    $$\text{Prob (rej)} = 1 - .05 = .95$$

    Choice *d.*

    (See section III.B Distributions)

14. *What value of z in the normal tables has 5% of the area in the tail beyond it?*
    a. 1.960
    b. 1.645
    c. 2.576
    d. 1.282

    The correct answer is *b*. Some common z values and their associated percentages are given below:

Z	%BELOW
-2.576	.5
-2.325	1.0
-1.960	2.5
-1.645	5.0
-1.282	10.0

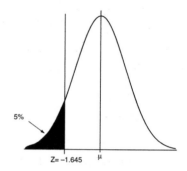

(See section III.B Distributions, and III.C Statistical inference)

15. *A large lot of parts is rejected by your customer and found, upon screening, to be 20% defective. What is the probability that the lot would have been accepted by the following sampling plan: sample size = 10; accept if no defectives; reject if one or more defectives?*
    a. .89
    b. .20
    c. .80
    d. .11
    e. None of the above

    The easiest way to compute this is to note that for sampling with replacement ("large lot")

    Prob (0 defective) = Prob (#1 good) Prob (#2 good)
    $\ldots$ Prob (#10 good) = $(1 - .2)^{10}$ = .107 $\cong$ .11

    Choice *d*.
    (See section III.B Distributions)

16. *An operation requires shipments from your vendor of small lots of fixed size. The attribute sampling plan used for receiving inspection should have its OC curve developed using*
    a. the Binomial distribution.
    b. the Gaussian (normal) distribution.
    c. the Poisson distribution.
    d. the Hypergeometric distribution.

    Since the question refers to attribute sampling we can rule out choice *b*, which applies to variables data. Choices *a* and *c* assume large lots. The hypergeometric distribution is the correct choice for small isolated lots and attribute inspection, choice *d*.
    (See section III.B Distributions)

17. *The expression* $P(x) = \dfrac{u^x e^{-u}}{x!}$ *the general term for the*

    a. Poisson distribution.
    b. Pascal distribution
    c. Hypergeometric distribution.
    d. Binomial distribution.

    The expression is the probability density function of the Poisson distribution, choice *a*. In a typical quality control application u would be the average rate of defects-per-unit and x would be the defect count. With this sort of question you must read the question with extreme care, previous exams have had equations that differ from a well known distribution in only a very small (but vital) detail.
    (See section III.B Distributions)

18. **Which table should be used to determine a confidence interval on the mean when s is not known and the sample size is 10?**

     a. z

     b. t

     c. F

     d. x^2

The t tables are used to place confidence bounds on the mean based on small sample sizes. The bounds are

$$\overline{X} - t_{1-\frac{\alpha}{2}}\frac{s}{\sqrt{n}} < \mu < \overline{X} + t_{1-\frac{\alpha}{2}}\frac{s}{\sqrt{n}}$$

Choice *b* is correct.

(See section III.C Statistical inference)

19. **A purchaser wants to determine whether or not there is any difference between the means of the convolute paperboard cans supplied by two different vendors, A and B. A random sample of 100 cans is selected from the output of each vendor. The sample from A yielded a mean of 13.59 with a standard deviation of 5.94. The sample from B yielded a mean of 14.43 with a standard deviation of 5.61. Which of the following would be a suitable null hypothesis to test?**

     a. $\mu_A = \mu_B$

     b. $\mu_A > \mu_B$

     c. $\mu_A < \mu_B$

     d. $\mu_A \neq \mu_B$

The question states: "A purchaser wants to determine whether or not there is any difference between the means . . ." The null hypothesis $\mu_A = \mu_B$ is correct. Choice *a*. Choice *d* is the alternate hypothesis.

(See section III.C Statistical inference)

20. *A null hypothesis assumes that a process is producing no more than the maximum allowable rate of defective items. The type II error is to conclude that the process:*
     a. is producing too many defectives when it actually isn't.
     b. is not producing too many defectives when it actually is.
     c. is not producing too many defectives when it is not.
     d. is producing too many defectives when it is.

     The Type II error is the probability that a hypothesis that is false will be accepted. The null hypothesis will be false when the process is producing too many defectives. Thus the correct answer is *b*.
     (See section III.C Statistical inference)

21. *Which of the following cannot be a null hypothesis?*
     a. the population means are equal.
     b. p' = 0.5
     c. the sample means are equal.
     d. the difference in the population means is 3.85

     Null hypotheses refer to *population,* not samples (see question 51 in this section for an example). Thus choice *c* can not be a null hypothesis.
     (See section III.C Statistical inference)

22. *You have been doing precision testing on a special order micrometer delivered by a vendor. The sample size in your test was 25 readings. The acceptance specification requires a precision sigma of .003 inch. Your observed precision sigma was .0033 inch. Although the observed precision did not meet the requirements, you are reluctant to reject it because you need it badly. You should:*
     a. accept it because it is close enough.
     b. reject it because it did not meet the criteria.
     c. apply the Chi-square test to see if the micrometer should be accepted.
     d. apply the F test to see if the micrometer should be accepted.
     e. send the micrometer to the gage lab for adjustment.

The correct statistical test to apply when testing the hypothesis that a population standard deviation is less than or equal to a "target" standard deviation is the Chi-square test. The null hypothesis is

$$H : \sigma = \sigma_0$$

where σ = The population standard deviation

σ_0 = The target standard deviation

for our case here $\sigma_0 = .003$. The test statistic

$$X^2 = \frac{(n-1)s^2}{\sigma_0^2} = \frac{24(.0033)^2}{(.003)^2}$$

has a Chi-square distribution with 24 degrees of freedom. Choice *c* is correct.

(See section III.C Statistical inference)

23. *If, in a t-test, alpha is .05,*
   a. 5% of the time we will say that there is no real difference, but in reality there is a difference.
   b. 5% of the time we will make a correct inference.
   c. 5% of the time we will say that there is a real difference when there really is not a difference.
   d. 95% of the time we will make an incorrect inference.
   e. 95% of the time the null hypothesis will be correct.

Alpha, also known as Type I error or level of significance, is the probability of rejecting the null hypothesis when it is actually true. In a t test we are testing a hypothesis regarding the equality of two means based on samples, namely,

$$H : \mu_1 = \mu_2$$

If $\alpha = .05$ then we will reject the null hypothesis (i.e. say there is a difference) when in fact the null hypothesis is true (i.e. there is no difference) 5% of the time. This is choice *c*.

(See section III.C Statistical inference)

24. *Quality assurance plans for computer software packages should include all of the following elements* **except:**
    a. accurate and complete documentation of programs.
    b. test criteria and test procedures.
    c. provision of alternate packages.
    d. testing under real life conditions.

    Choice *c* is not an appropriate quality assurance element.
    (See section III.C Statistical inference, and III.D Correlation and regression analysis)

25. *A study was conducted on the relationship between the speed of different cars and their gasoline mileage. The correlation coefficient was found to be 0.35. Later, it was discovered that there was a defect in the speedometers and they had all been set 5 miles per hour too fast. The correlation coefficient was computed using the corrected scores. Its new value will be*
    a. 0.30
    b. 0.35
    c. 0.40
    d. -.35

    The simple correlation coefficient is given by the equation

    $$r = \frac{\sum_{i=1}^{n}(X_i - \overline{X})(Y_i - \overline{Y})}{\sqrt{\sum_{i=1}^{n}(X_i - \overline{X})^2 \sum_{i=1}^{n}(Y_i - \overline{Y})^2}}$$

    An illustration is shown below.

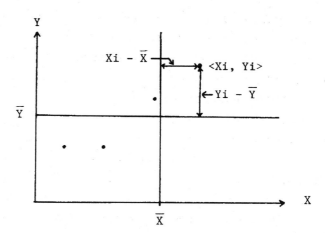

If all the speedometers are set 5 m.p.h. too fast it would have the effect of shifting all Y_i's down by 5 units. However, $\overline{Y}$ would also drop by 5 so the *sums of differences* ($Y_i - \overline{Y}$) would not change. Also, the sums of differences $X_i - \overline{X}$ are unchanged by the defect. Therefore r is unchanged and remains .35, choice *b*.
(See section III.D Correlation and regression analysis)

26. *The laboratory has notified the Quality Engineer of an incoming product which has changed from acceptable to marginal over a period of six months. Which of the following actions should taken?*
    1. Notify the laboratory to check their analysis and send a sample to an outside laboratory to verify the results.
    2. Notify the supplier of your observations and concern about the acceptability of his product.
    3. Notify receiving to reject the product based on the product's trend toward unacceptability.
  a. 1 and 2 only
  b. 1 and 3 only
  c. 2 and 3 only
  d. 1, 2 and 3

Again, as happens so often, option *c* is not correct (the product is *marginal*, not yet unacceptable) and choice *a* is the only one that doesn't include this option. Thus choice *a*.
(See section III.D Correlation and regression analysis)

27. *All of the following statements are true except:*
    a. in multiple regression, extrapolation beyond the region of observations can lead to erroneous predications.
    b. at least 3 variables are involved in multiple regression.
    c. multiple regression involves one independent and two or more dependent variables.

    The multiple regression model has one *dependent* variable and two or more *independent* variables. For example, a multiple linear regression model might be

    $$\hat{y} = a + b_1 x_1 + b_2 x_2 + \varepsilon$$

    where x_1, x_2 are independent variables, b_1 is the coefficient for x_1 and b_2 is the coefficient for x_2.
    Thus choice *c* is not incorrect.

    Extrapolation beyond the region of observation (data space) is always risky. Here is an example

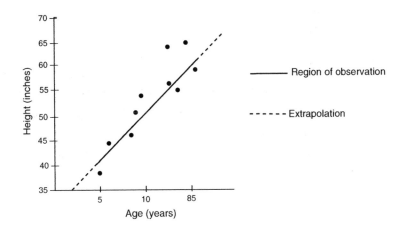

Based on this model we might project a 25 year old to be over 9 feet tall!

(See section III.D Correlation and regression analysis)

28. *A two-way Analysis of Variance has r levels for the one variable and c levels for the second variable with 2 observations per cell. The degrees of freedom for interaction is*
   a. 2 (r x c)
   b. (r - 1) (c - 1)
   c. rc - 1
   d. 2 (r - 1) (c - 1)

   The degrees of freedom for interaction for two-way Analysis of Variance is always $(r - 1)(c - 1)$, regardless of the number of observations per cell. Choice *b* is correct.

   (See section III.E Experimental design)

29. *The following coded results were obtained from a single factor, completely randomized experiment, in which the production outputs of the three machines (A, B, C) were to be compared.*

A.	4	8	5	7	6
B.	2	0	1	2	4
C.	-3	1	-2	-1	0

   What is the sum of squares for the error term?
   a. 170
   b. 130
   c. 40
   d. 14

   This will illustrate the calculations for the one-way Analysis of Variance (ANOVA) for the completely randomized single factor experiment:

		Total	N	Sum of Squares
Treatment A	4, 8, 5, 7,6 6	30	5	190
Treatment B	2, 0, 1, 2, 4	9	5	25
Treatment C	-3, 1, -2, -1, 0	-5	5	15
	Totals	34	15	230

$$\text{Total sum of squares } = \ 230 - \frac{(34)^2}{15} = 152.933$$

$$\text{Treatment sum of squares} = \frac{(30)^2}{5} + \frac{(9)^2}{5} + \frac{(-5)^2}{5} - \frac{(34)^2}{15} = 124.133$$

Error sum of squares

= Total sum of squares - Treatment sum of squares

= 152.933 - 124.133 = 28.8

The ANOVA Table is given below

ANOVA						
Source of variation	*SS*	*df*	*MS*	*F*	*P-value*	*F crit*
Machines	124.133	2	62.067	25.861	0.000	3.885
Error	28.800	12	2.400			
Total	152.933	14				

The probability that F is due to chance is less than .01. The answer given in the published exam is incorrect. However, if one of the "2's" in Treatment B is changed to "–2", answer *c* will result.

(See section III.E Experimental design)

30. *Consider the SS and MS columns of an Analysis of Variance table for a single factor design. The appropriate ratio for testing the null hypothesis of no treatment effect is*
   a. *SS treatments divided by SS residual.*
   b. *MS treatments divided by MS residual.*
   c. *SS treatments divided by MS residual.*
   d. *MS treatments divided by SS residual.*

   Refer to the example shown for the previous question. The correct choice is *b*. Note that the terms "residual" and "error" are synonymous. *(See section III.E Experimental design)*

31. *The results of a designed experiment are to be analyzed using a Chi-square test. There are five treatments under consideration and each observation falls into one of two categories (success or failure). The calculated value of Chi-square is compared to the tabulated Chi-square with how many degrees of freedom?*
   a. *10*
   b. *9*
   c. *5*
   d. *4*

   The degrees of freedom for analysis of contingency tables with r rows and c columns is (r–1) (c–1). In this problem we have 2 rows and 5 columns (or vice-versa)

	TREATMENT				
	1	2	3	4	5
Good					
Bad					

   Thus df = (2–1) (5–1) = 4
   Choice *d*.
   (See section III.E Experimental design)

32. *In performing an Analysis of Variance for a single factor experiment, a fundamental assumption which is made is that the factor*
     a. means are equal.
     b. means are unequal.
     c. variances are equal.
     d. variances are unequal.

     Homogeneity of variance, choice *c*, is a fundamental assumption underlying Analysis of Variance.
     (See section III.E Experimental design)

33. *Which of the following purposes are served by replicating an experiment?*
     1. Provide a means for estimating the experimental error.
     2. Increase the number of treatments included in the experiment.
     3. Improve the precision of estimates of treatment effects.
     a. 1 and 2 only
     b. 1 and 3 only
     c. 2 and 3 only
     d. 1, 2 and 3

     Increasing the number of observations by replicating an experiment provides the benefits described by 1 and 3; this means choice *b* is correct. Another way to arrive at this is to observe that 2 is untrue and that only choice *b* doesn't have 2.
     (See section III.E Experimental design)

34. Three trainees were given the same lot of 50 pieces and asked to classify them as defective or nondefective, with the following results:

	TRAINEE #1	TRAINEE #2	TRAINEE #3	TOTAL
Defective	17	30	25	72
Non-Defective	33	20	25	78
TOTAL	50	50	50	150

In determining whether or not there is a difference in the ability of the three trainees to properly classify the parts,
a. the value of Chi-square is about 6.
b. using a level of significance of 0.05, the critical value of Chi-square is 5.99.
c. since the obtained Chi-square is greater than 5.99, we reject the null hypothesis.
d. all of the above.
e. none of the above.

Refer to question 91 of this section for a reference that describes the method used to analyze the data. We first note that

$$\text{degrees of freedom} = (r-1)(c-1) = 2$$

and that Chi-square tables give a critical value of 5.97 for $\alpha = .05$. The Chi-square statistic is

$$\chi^2 = \sum_{\text{over all cells}} \frac{(\text{Frequency expected} - \text{Frequency observed})^2}{\text{Frequency expected}}$$

The sum is taken over all cells. Each cell $F_{expected}$ is computed as

$$F_{expected}(cell) = \frac{\text{Row total x Column total}}{\text{Grand total}}$$

This gives the table below:

Expected frequencies.

	TRAINEE #1	TRAINEE #2	TRAINEE #3
Defective	$\dfrac{(50)(72)}{150} = 24$	24	24
Non-Defective	$\dfrac{(50)(78)}{150} = 26$	26	26

$$X^2 = \frac{(17-24)^2}{24} + \frac{(30-24)^2}{24} + \frac{(25-24)^2}{24}$$
$$+ \frac{(33-26)^2}{26} + \frac{(20-26)^2}{26} + \frac{(25-26)^2}{26} = 6.89$$

Obviously choices *b* and *c* are correct. If we accept that 6.89 is "about 6" the answer is given by choice *d*, which is the official answer.
(See section III.E Experimental design)

35. *The test used for testing significance in an Analysis of Variance table:*
a. *the z test.*
b. *the t test.*
c. *the F test.*
d. *the Chi-square test.*

The F test is used to test the hypothesis that two sample variances are equal. This is correct for the Analysis of Variance (ANOVA) since we compare the within group variance to the between group variances. Choice *c* is correct. (Note: ANOVA is a test of the equality of *means*, not variances.)
(See section III.E Experimental design)

36. *In a single factor analysis of variance, the assumption of homogeneity of variances applies to:*
     a. the variances within the treatment groups.
     b. the variance of the treatment means.
     c. the total variance.
     d. all of the above.

     In single factor (or any other) analysis of variance we assume the *within group* variance is homogeneous, i.e. it doesn't change from group to group. Choice *a* is correct. This assumption is vital to the validity of the tests of hypotheses. Statistical tests exist to check this assumption.
     (See section III.E Experimental design)

37. *A 3^2 experiment means that we are considering:*
     a. two levels of three factors.
     b. two dependent variables and three independent variables.
     c. two go/no-go variables and three continuous variables.
     d. three levels of two factors.

     Standard notation for designed experiments where there are n factors all at L levels is L^n. Thus choice *d* is correct.
     (See section III.E Experimental design)

38. *Basic assumptions underlying the Analysis of Variance include*
     1. observations are from normally distributed populations.
     2. observations are from populations with equal variances.
     3. observations are from populations with equal means.
     a. 1 and 2 only
     b. 1 and 3 only
     c. 2 and 3 only
     d. 1, 2 and 3

     Choices 1 and 2 are the basic assumptions. Choice 3 is the null hypothesis we usually test with ANOVA. Thus option *a* is best.
     (See section III.E Experimental design)

39. *The primary advantage of the Latin Square design, compared to the factorial design, is that*
    a. it requires less data.
    b. it eliminates the need for interaction analysis.
    c. it allows higher significance levels.
    d. it does not require homogeneity of variance.

    The factorial design provides a means of testing for *interaction* effects, while the Latin Square does not. The additional information requires additional data for factorial designs, making choice *a* correct. Latin Square designs do not "eliminate the need for interaction analysis," they do, however, assume that interaction effects are negligible.
    (See section III.E Experimental design)

40. *To state that a model in an experimental design is fixed indicates that*
    a. the levels used for each factor are the only ones of interest.
    b. the levels were chosen from a fixed population.
    c. the equipment from which the data are collected must not be moved.
    d. the factors under consideration are qualitative.

    There are two types of factors in any experiment, fixed and random. A fixed factor is one where all levels of interest of the factor are chosen. For example, if the experiment involves a 4 spindle drill and all four spindles are considered. A random factor is one where *only a sample* of all possible levels are tried. An example would be an experiment that gathers data from 5 machines when the intent is to extrapolate the results to 10 other machines. Choice *a* is correct.
    (See section III.E Experimental design)

41. *An experiment with two factors, in which all levels of one variable are run at each level of the second variable, is called a*
   a. one-way experiment.
   b. Latin square experiment.
   c. factorial experiment.
   d. fractional factorial experiment.

   The answer is *c*. These experiments are sometimes called *full factorial* experiments to distinguish them from fractional factorial experiments. A fractional factorial experiment is one where only some of the possible factor combinations tried, an example is shown below.

Fractional factorial experiment.

This is a half fraction of a three factor experiment, each factor at 2 levels. Standard notation: 2^{3-1} experiment.
(See section III.E Experimental design)

The following paragraph refers to questions 42, 43, and 44.

Lots of 75 parts each are inspected to an AQL of 0.2% using normal inspection, single sampling. A single lower specification limit, denoted by 'L,' is used. The standard level (Level II in MIL-STD-105E, Level IV in MIL-STD-414) is specified. The following 3 questions require that you have a copy of MIL-STD-105 (or ANSI/ASQC Z1.4) and MIL-STD-414 (or ANSI/ASQC Z1.9) handy.

42. The sample size for MIL-STD-105E is:
  a. 13
  b. 32
  c. 50
  d. 75

To get the answer we begin by entering Table I for a lot size of 75, Level II inspection. We find sample size code letter E.

Table I. Sample size code letters.

Lot or Batch Size	Special Inspection Levels				General Inspection Levels		
	S–1	S–2	S–3	S–4	I	II	III
26 to 50	A	B	B	C	C	D	E
51 t0 90	B	B	C	C	C	E	F
91 to 150	B	B	C	D	D	F	G

This value is taken to Table II.A where we find the row for code letter E and the column for .25% AQL.

Table II.A. Single sampling plans for normal inspection.

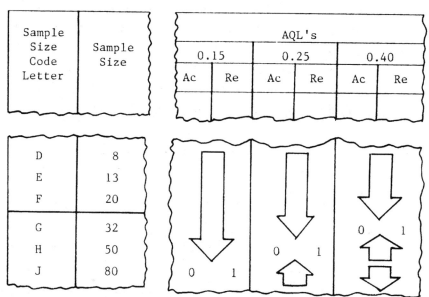

The arrows take us from the code letter E row to the code letter H row, for the sample size of 50. Choice *c* is correct.
(See section III.F Acceptance sampling)

43. *The sample size for MIL-STD-414, estimating variability by the range method, is:*

a. *3*

b. *7*

c. *10*

d. *15*

e. *20*

MIL-STD-414 is the department of defense standard for inspection by variables for percent defective.

Several past CQE exams have had questions that require an understanding of this standard. You should be aware that the ANSI/ASQC Z1.9-1980 "equivalent" to MIL-STD-414 is not identical (for example, it will give a different answer to this problem.) You may wish to take both standards with you when you take the exam and use the standard actually referred to in the question.

We begin by entering Table A.2 of MIL-STD-414

LOT SIZE	INSPECTION LEVEL				
	I	II	III	IV	V
. . .	. . .	. . .	. . .	. . .	. . .
41 to 65	B	B	C	E	G
66 to 110	B	B	D	F	H
111 to 180	B	C	E	G	I
. . .	. . .	. . .	. . .	. . .	. . .

The correct row and column are shown in bold, which gives sample code letter F. Our next step is to enter Table C.1 (we assume variability unknown since we are not told otherwise.)

Table C.1. Master table for normal and tightened inspection: Variability unknown. (Single Specification Limit—Form 1)

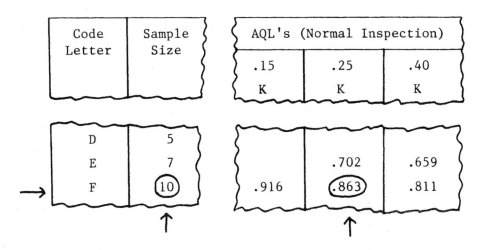

We get our sample size as 10, which is choice *c*.
(See section III.F Acceptance sampling)

44. *The acceptance criterion, using MIL-STD-414 and the range method is: Accept the lot if...*
   a. *$(\overline{X} - L)/R \geq 0.702$*
   b. *$(\overline{X} - L)/R \geq 0.863$*
   c. *$(\overline{X} - L)/R \geq 1.06$*
   d. *$(\overline{X} - L)/R \leq 1.06$*

   Refer to the table shown in question 43. When form 1, section C, is used, the acceptance criterion is

   $$(\overline{X} - L)/R \geq K$$

   The table gives K = 0.863, choice *b*.
   (See section III.F Acceptance sampling)

45. *A comparison of known sigma and unknown sigma variables plans will show that equal protection is obtained (as determined by the OC curves):*
   a. *when the unknown sigma sample size is smaller than the known sigma sample size.*
   b. *when the known sigma sample size is larger than the unknown sigma size.*
   c. *when the known sigma and unknown sigma sample sizes are equal.*
   d. *none of these.*

   In general, less data is required for equal protection if sigma is known. This selection is not offered, thus choice *d* is correct.
   (See section III.F Acceptance sampling)

46. *Using MIL-STD-105E, what sample size should be taken from a lot of 1000 pieces for inspection level II with normal inspection?*
   a. *32*
   b. *50*
   c. *80*
   d. *100*
   e. *125*

   Actually this question is missing some important items; these are

- Single, double, or multiple sampling?
- What AQL? (For a proper question on MIL-STD-105E see question 42)

If we just find the sample size code letter (see question 42) and use this in the master table for single normal sampling, we get a sample size of 80. This is the "official" answer, choice *c*.
(See section III.F Acceptance sampling)

47. *In deciding whether sampling inspection of parts would be more economical than 100% inspection, you need to determine all of the following* except:
   a. cost of inspecting the parts.
   b. cost of correcting defective parts.
   c. cost of not *finding defective parts.*
   d. cost of improving the production process.

   Inspection, by acceptance sampling methods or by 100% screening, is a *detection* oriented activity that is taken based on the currect process. The correct choice is *d*. This is not to say that the process shouldn't be improved, process improvement should be an ongoing activity. In fact, it can be shown that under quite general conditions the optimal amount of inspection is *always* either 100% inspection or zero inspection.
   (See section III.F Acceptance sampling)

48. *In MIL-STD-105E, the AQL is always determined at what P_a on the OC curve?*
   a. 0.05
   b. 0.10
   c. 0.90
   d. 0.95
   e. none of the above.

   With MIL-STD-105E the probability of acceptance (P_a) given an AQL (Acceptable Quality Level) process varies. The answer is *e*.
   (See section III.F Acceptance sampling)

49. *The Dodge-Romig Tables are designed to minimize which parameter?*
    a. AOQL
    b. AQL
    c. ATI
    d. AOQ

    Dodge-Romig tables contain single and double acceptance sampling plans that minimize the Average Total Inspected (ATI) subject to a constrained Average Outgoing Quality Limit (AOQL) or Lot Tolerance Percent Defective (LTPD). The correct choice is *c*.
    (See section III.F Acceptance sampling)

50. *The acronym "AQL," as used in sampling inspection, means:*
    a. that level of lot quality for which there is a small risk of rejecting the lot.
    b. the Average Quality Limit.
    c. the maximum percent defective that can be considered satisfactory as a process average.
    d. the quality level.

    The term AQL, or acceptable quality level, is defined in Military Standard 105E as

    "the maximum percent defective (or defects per hundred units) that, for purposes of sampling inspection, can be considered satisfactory as a process average." Thus *c* is correct. Note: choice *c* erroneously leaves off the crucial qualifier phrase "for purposes of sampling inspection."
    (See section III.F Acceptance sampling)

51. *An operating characteristic curve shows:*
    a. the probability of accepting lots of various quality levels by sampling methods.
    b. the operating characteristics of a machine.
    c. how to operate a machine for best quality results.

d. the probability that a lot contains a certain number of rejectable parts.

An operating characteristics curve (OC curve) is shown below. The vertical axis shows the probability of accepting the null hypothesis using a sampling scheme, the horizontal axis shows the actual "state of nature." In a typical quality control application the state of nature would be the process quality levels. This makes choice *a* the best.

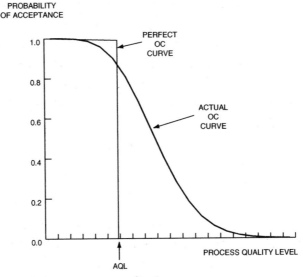

(See section III.F Acceptance sampling)

52. ***Two quantities which uniquely determine a single sampling attributes plan are***
   a. AQL and LTPD.
   b. sample size and rejection number.
   c. AQL and producer's risk.
   d. LTPD and consumer's risk.

   The sample size and rejection number uniquely determine a single attributes sampling plan. All of the other choices are operating characteristics.

   (See section III.F Acceptance sampling)

53. *In comparison with attributes sampling plans, variables sampling plans*
    a. *have the advantage of greater simplicity.*
    b. *usually require a larger sample size for comparable assurance as to the correctness of decisions in judging a single quality characteristic.*
    c. *have the advantage of being applicable to either single or multiple quality characteristics.*
    d. *provide greater assurance, for the same sample size, as to the correctness of decisions in judging a single quality characteristic.*

    Choice *d* is correct. The converse is also true; that is, for a given level of assurance a variables sampling plan requires a smaller sample size.
    (See section III.F Acceptance sampling)

54. *How many outcomes are possible when performing a single trial of a binomial experiment?*
    a. *one.*
    b. *two.*
    c. *three.*

    By definition, there are two possible outcomes from a single trial of a binomial experiment, choice *b*. A typical quality control example would be an inspection of a unit where the unit is to be classified as either conforming or non-conforming.
    (See section III.F Acceptance sampling)

55. *Under acceptance sampling, with screening, average outgoing quality will not be worse, in the long run, than the*
    a. *ATI*
    b. *AQL*
    c. *AOQL*
    d. *AOQ*

    When acceptance sampling is performed and rejected lots are 100% inspected, with defectives removed or replaced with non-defectives, the average outgoing quality (AOQ) is related to the incoming quality. There is a maximum average outgoing quality for all possible incoming quality levels, known as the average outgoing quality limit or AOQL. This is choice *c*.

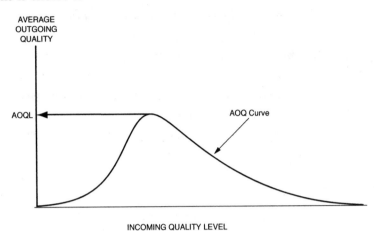

(See section III.F Acceptance sampling)

56. *A comparison of variable and attribute sampling systems will show that equal protection (as determined by the OC curves) can be obtained:*
    a. when the variable and attribute sample size are equal.
    b. when the attribute sample is smaller than the variable sample.
    c. when the variable sample is smaller than the attribute sample.
    d. none of these.

    Choice *c* is correct. Also see question 53 in this chapter.
    (See section III.F Acceptance sampling)

57. *Why would inspection by variables be superior to inspection by attributes?*

> 1. *Inspection by variables is easier to administer than inspection by attributes.*
>
> 2. *More information is obtained when inspection by variables is utilized.*
>
> 3. *Inspection by variables usually requires smaller samples than inspection by attributes.*

a. *2 only*

b. *3 only*

c. *1 and 2 only*

d. *1, 2 and 3*

The "official" answer is choice *a*, 2 only. "2" is certainly true since variables data provides information about centering, spread, distribution shape, outliers, etc. that are not provided by attributes data. However, since variables plans provide protection equal to attributes plans with smaller sample sizes (see questions #53 and #56 in this chapter), one could argue in favor of choice *b* (3 only). My personal opinion is that "2 and 3 only" would be the best, but this choice isn't offered.

(See section III.F Acceptance sampling)

C. ANSWERS TO SELECTED PAST EXAM QUESTIONS

1. *The sum of the squared deviations of a group of measurements from their mean divided by the number of measurements equals:*

a. σ

b. σ^2

c. *zero*

d. *X*

e. *the mean deviation*

(Answer: b.)

2. *In determining a process average fraction defective using inductive or inferential statistics, we use* _____ *computed from* _____ *to make inferences about* _____ .
   a. *statistics, samples, populations*
   b. *populations, samples, populations*
   c. *samples, statistics, populations*
   d. *samples, populations, samples*
   e. *statistics, populations, statistics*
   (Answer: **a.**)

3. *Which of the following statistical measures of variability is* not *dependent on the exact value of every measurement?*
   a. *interquartile range* .
   b. *variance.*
   c. *range.*
   d. *coefficient of variation.*
   e. *none of the above.*
   (Answer: **c.**)

4. *If X and Y are distributed normally and independently, the variance of X-Y is equal to;*
   a. $\sigma_x^2 + \sigma_y^2$

   b. $\sigma_x - \sigma_y^2$

   c. $\sqrt{\sigma_x^2 + \sigma^{y2}}$

   d. $\sqrt{\sigma_y^2 - \sigma_y^2}$

   (Answer: **a.** *See section III.A Terms and concepts. Note: the published answer,* $\sigma_x^2 2 \sigma_y^2$, *is a typo.*)

5. The mean of either a discrete or a continuous distribution can always be visualized as:
    a. the point where 50% of the values are to the left side and 50% are to the right side.
    b. its center of gravity.
    c. the point where the most values in the distribution occur.
    d. all of the above.
    (Answer: b.)

6. Given 6 books how many sets can be arranged in lots of 3 but always in a different order?
    a. 18 sets.
    b. 54 sets.
    c. 108 sets.
    d. 120 sets.
    (Answer: d, a permutation.)

7. Determine the coefficient of variation for the last 500 pilot plant test runs of high temperature film having a mean of 900° Kelvin with a standard deviation of 54°:
    a. 6%
    b. 16.7%
    c. 0.06%
    d. 31%
    e. the reciprocal of the relative standard deviation
    (Answer: a. See Appendix 4.)

8. *Suppose that 5 bad electron tubes get mixed up with 8 good tubes. If 2 tubes are drawn simultaneously, what is the probability that both are good?*
   a. 8/13
   b. 14/39
   c. 7/12
   d. 7/13
   e. 36/91
   (Answer: b. See section III.B.4 Binomial, Poisson, hypergeometric, ...)

9. *A process is turning out end-items which have defects of Type A or Type B or both in them. If the probability of a Type A defect is .10 and of a Type B defect is .20, the probability that an end item will have no defects is:*
   a. .02
   b. .28
   c. .30
   d. .72
   e. .68
   (Answer: d. See section III.B.4 Binomial, Poisson, hypergeometric, ...)

10. *When performing calculations on sample data:*
    a. the cumulative relative frequency graph that is often used is called a histogram.
    b. rounding the data has no effect on the mean and standard deviation.
    c. coding the data has no effect on the mean and standard deviation.
    d. coding and rounding affect both the mean and standard deviation.
    (Answer: d. See section III.A Terms and concepts)

11. *Three parts are additive to an assembly. Their design specifications for length and tolerance are 0.240 ± 0.006, 0.3200 ± 0.0006, and 1.360 ± 0.003 respectively. Assume that each of the distributions is normal.*

*Combine these dimensions statistically to give a final length and
tolerance to three decimal places*

a. 1.360 ± 0.006
b. 0.799 ± 0.565
c. 0.640 ± 0.010
d. 1.920 ± 0.007

*(Answer: **d**. Hint:* $\sigma \approx \dfrac{\text{Tolerance}}{6}$, $\sigma_{sum}^2 = \sum \sigma^2.$ *)*

12. *Estimate the variance of the population from which the following
sample data came: 22, 18, 17, 20, 21.*

    a. 4.3
    b. 2.1
    c. 1.9
    d. 5.0

    *(Answer: **a**.)*

13. *Calculate the standard deviation of the following complete set of data:
52, 20, 24, 31, 35, 42.*

    a. 10.8
    b. 11.8
    c. 12.8
    d. 13.8

    *(Answer: **a**.)*

14. *If X and Y are dependent random variables, and if X has variance 4
and Y has variance 3, then the variance of 5X – Y is:*

    a. 103
    b. 23
    c. 17
    d. Unknown

    *(Answer: **d**. The key word is* dependent.*)*

15. *A random variable:*
    a. may be either discrete or continuous.
    b. is called "random" because it depends on the normal distribution.
    c. is called "variable" because it refers to the variance.
    d. is all of the above.
    (Answer: a.)

16. *Which one of the following is a true statement of probability?*
    a. P(E and F) = P(E) + P(F).
    b. P(E or F) = P(E) • P(E/F)
    c. P(E or F) = P(E) + P(F) − P(E and F).
    d P(E and F) = P(E) + P(F) − P(E and F).
    (Answer: c.)

17. *A parameter is:*
    a. a random variable.
    b. a sample value
    c. a population value.
    d the solution to a statistical problem.
    (Answer: c.)

18. *A statistic is:*
    a. the solution to a problem.
    b. a population value.
    c. a positive number between 0 and 1 inclusive.
    d. a sample value.
    (Answer: d.)

19. *A frequency polygon:*
    a. *is a plot of connected points whose ordinates are proportional to cell frequencies.*
    b. *is also known as a cumulative relative frequency graph.*
    c. *is also known as a sample distribution function.*
    d. *applies only to discrete random variables.*
    (Answer: a.)

20. *The standard deviation as a percent of the mean is called:*
    a. *relative precision.*
    b. *coefficient of variability.*
    c. *standard deviation of the mean.*
    d. *standard error.*
    (Answer: b.)

21. *If a distribution is skewed to the left the median will always be:*
    a. *less than the mean.*
    b. *between the mean and the mode.*
    c. *greater than the mode.*
    d. *equal to the mean.*
    e. *equal to the mode.*
    (Answer: b.)

22. *The expression* $\dfrac{u^x \cdot e^{-\mu}}{x!}$ *is the general term for the:*
    a. *Hypergeometric distribution.*
    b. *Pascal distribution.*
    c. *Poisson distribution.*
    d. *Binomial distribution.*
    e. *none of the above.*
    (Answer: c.)

23. *If, in a t-test alpha is .01:*
    a. *1% of the time we will say that there is a real difference, when there really is not a difference.*
    b. *1% of the time we will make a correct inference.*
    c. *1% of the time we will say that there is no real difference, but in reality there is a difference.*
    d. *99% of the time we will make an incorrect inference.*
    e. *99% of the time the null hypothesis will be correct.*
    (Answer: a.)

24. *One use for a Student t-test is to determine whether or not differences exist in:*
    a. *variability.*
    b. *quality costs.*
    c. *correlation coefficients.*
    d. *averages.*
    e. *none of these.*
    (Answer: d.)

25. *The probability of observing at least one defective in a random sample of size ten drawn from a population that has been producing, on the average, ten percent defective units is:*
    a. $(0.10)^{10}$
    b. $(0.90)^{10}$
    c. $1 - (0.10)^{10}$
    d. $1 - (0.90)^{10}$
    e. $(0.10)(0.90)^{9}$
    (Answer: d. See section III.B Distributions. Hint: binomial distribution.)

26. *Large panes of plate glass contain on the average 0.25 flaws per pane. The standard deviation of the distribution of flaws is:*

    a. .25

    b. .05

    c. .50

    d. .75

    e. none of the above.

    (Answer: c. See III.B Distributions. For the Poisson, $\sigma = \sqrt{\text{average}}$)

27. *The lengths of a certain bushing are normally distributed with mean $\overline{X}'$. How many standard deviation units, symmetrical about $\overline{X}'$, will include 80% of the lengths?*

    a. ± 1.04

    b. ± 0.52

    c. ± 1.28

    d. ± 0.84

    (Answer: c. See section III.B Distributions. Use Appendix Table 5.)

28. *Three trainees were given the same lot of 50 pieces and asked to classify them as defective or non-defective with the following results:*

	TRAINEE #1	TRAINEE #2	TRAINEE #3	TOTAL
Defective	17	30	25	72
Non-Defective	33	20	25	78
Total	50	50	50	150

In determining whether or not there is a difference in the ability of the three trainees to properly classify the parts:

a. the value of chi-square is about 6.90.

b. using a level of significance of 0.05, the critical value of chi-square is 5.99.

c. since the obtained chi-square is greater than 5.99, we reject the null hypothesis.

d. all of the above.

e. none of the above.

*(Answer: **d**. See section III.B Distributions. Also see question 33 in section B of this chapter.)*

29. *A process is producing material which is 40% defective. Four pieces are selected at random for inspection. What is the probability of exactly one good piece being found in the sample?*

    a. .870

    b. .575

    c. .346

    d. .130

    e. .154

    *(Answer: **e**. See section III.B Distributions. This is Binomial.)*

30. *An inspection plan is set up to randomly sample 3' of a 100' cable and accept the cable if no flaws are found in the 3' length. What is the probability that a cable with an average of 1 flaw per foot will be rejected by the plan?*

    a. .05

    b. .95

    c. .72

    d. .03

    e. .10

    *(Answer: **b**. See section III.B Distributions. This is Poisson.)*

31. *Determine whether the following two types of rockets have significantly different variances at the 5% level.*

Rocket 1	Rocket 2
61 readings	31 readings
1,346.89 miles^2	2,237.29 miles^2

a. significant difference because Fcalc < F table.
b. no significant difference because Fcalc < F table.
c. significant difference because Fcalc > F table.
d. no significant difference because Fcalc < F table.
*(Answer: **b.**)*

32. *When using the Poisson as an approximation to the binomial the following conditions apply for the best approximation:*
    a. larger sample size and larger fraction defective.
    b. larger sample size and smaller fraction defective.
    c. smaller sample size and larger fraction defective.
    d. smaller sample size and smaller fraction defective.
    *(Answer: **b.**)*

33. *Given that random samples of process A produced 10 defective and 30 good units, while process B produced 25 defectives out of 60 units. Using the chi-square test, what is the probability that the observed value of chi-square could result, under the hypothesis that both processes are operating at the same quality level?*
    a. less than 5 percent.
    b. between 5 percent and 10 percent.
    c. greater than 10 percent.
    d. 50 percent.
    *(Answer: **b.**)*

34. *How many degrees of freedom should you use in the above problem?*
    a. 1
    b. 2
    c. 3
    d. 4
    *(Answer: **a.**)*

35. On the basis of the data in the previous problem, what would you conclude?

    a. Nothing. The facts involving the consequences of a wrong decision are unknown.

    b. The two processes are comparable .

    c. The two processes are significantly different.

    d. Reject the null hypothesis.

    (Answer: a.)

36. Assume a large lot contains exactly 4 percent defective items. Using the Poisson distribution, what is the probability that a random sample of 50 items will not reflect the true lot quality?

    a. 27%

    b. 73%

    c. 82%

    d. 67%

    (Answer: b.)

37. If the probability of a success on a single trial is 0.2, and 3 trials are performed, what is the probability of at least one success?

    a. 0.008

    b. 0.384

    c. 0.488

    d. 0.600

    (Answer: c. See section III.B Distributions. This is Binomial.)

38. A process is acceptable if its standard deviation is not greater than 1.0. A sample of four items yields the values 52, 56, 53, 55. In order to determine if the process be accepted or rejected, the following statistical test should be used:

    a. t-test.

    b. Chi-square test.

c. *Z-test.*
d. *none of the above.*
(Answer: b.)

39. *In a normal distribution, what is the area under the curve between +0.7 and +1.3 standard deviation units?*
    a. *0.2903*
    b. *0 7580*
    c. *0.2580*
    d. *0.1452*
    (Answer: d. See section III.B Distributions. Also see Appendix Table 5.)

40. *Two balance scales are to be compared by weighing the same five items on each scale, yielding the following results:*

ITEM	#1	#2	#3	#4	#5
Scale A	110	99	112	85	99
Scale B	112	101	113	88	101

The sharpest test comparing mean effects is obtained by using which one of the following:
a. *paired data test of significance with 4 degrees of freedom.*

b. $t = \dfrac{\overline{X}_A - \overline{X}_B}{S_\rho / \sqrt{n}}$ *for 8 degrees of freedom.*

c. *analysis of variance for randomized blocks.*
d. *determining the correlation coefficient r.*
(Answer: a.)

41. *How many standard deviation units, symmetrical about the mean, will span an area around the mean of 40 percent of the total area under the normal curve?*
    a. *±0.84*
    b *±0.52*

c ±*1.28*

d -0.25

(Answer: b. See section III.B Distributions. Also see Appendix Table 5.)

42. **The hypergeometric distribution is:**
    a. used to describe sampling without replacement from a finite population where there are several outcomes for each trial.
    b. a continuous distribution.
    c. a discrete distribution with its expected value equal to its variance.
    d. the limiting distribution of the sum of several independent discrete random variables.
    (Answer: a.)

43. **Ratios of two variances drawn from the same normal population are described by which one of the following distributions?**
    a. F.
    b. Student's "t".
    c. Chi-square.
    d. Normal.
    (Answer: a.)

44. **The binomial distribution is a discrete distribution and may be used to describe:**
    a. sampling without replacement from a finite population.
    b. the case of n independent trials with probabilities constant from trial to trial.
    c. the case of n independent trials with several outcomes for each trial.
    d. sampling without replacement from a finite population where there are several outcomes for each trial.
    (Answer: b.)

45. *This expression* $\dfrac{n!}{x!(n-X)!}\rho'^{X}(1-\rho')^{n-X}$ *is the following:*

a. *general term for the Poisson distribution.*
b. *general term for the Pascal distribution.*
c. *general term for the binomial distribution.*
d. *general term for the hypergeometric distribution.*
(Answer: c.)

46. *Suppose that, given X = 50 and Z = ± 1.96, we established 95% confidence limits for μ of 30 and 70. This means that:*
a. *the probability that μ = 50 is .05.*
b. *the probability that μ = 50 is .95.*
c. *the probability that the interval contains μ is .05.*
d. *the probability that the interval contains μ is .95.*
e. *none of the above.*
(Answer: d.)

47. *A null hypothesis requires several assumptions, a basic one of which is:*
a. *that the variables are dependent.*
b. *that the variables are independent.*
c. *that the sample size is adequate.*
d. *that the confidence interval is ± 2 standard deviation.*
e. *that the correlation coefficient is -0.95.*
(Answer: b.)

48. *A bin contains 40 pills with a weight of 3.1 gm each; 30 pills weighing 3.2 gms; 10 pills weighing 3.3 gms. The weight of an average pill is found from:*

a. $\dfrac{3.1+3.2+3.3}{3}$

b. $\dfrac{(3.1)(40)+(3.2)(30)+(3.3)(10)}{3}$

c. $\dfrac{(3.1+3.2+3.3)(10+30+40)}{80}$

d. $\dfrac{(3.1)(40)+(3.2)(30)+(3.3)(10)}{80}$

*(Answer: **d**.)*

49. *If it was known that a population of 30,000 parts had a standard deviation of .05 seconds, what size sample would be required to maintain an error no greater than .01 seconds with a confidence level of 95%?*
    a. *235*
    b. *487*
    c. *123*
    d. *96*
    e. *78*
    *(Answer: **d**. You can ignore the population size.)*

50. *When finding a confidence interval for mean* μ *based on a sample size of n:*
    a. *increasing n increases the interval.*
    b. *having to use* s_x *instead of* σ *decreases the interval.*
    c. *the larger the interval, the better the estimate of* μ.
    d. *increasing n decreases the interval.*
    *(Answer: **d**.)*

51. *The beta risk is the risk of:*
    a. *selecting the wrong hypothesis.*
    b. *accepting an hypothesis when it is false.*
    c. *accepting an hypothesis when it is true*
    d *rejecting an hypothesis when it is true.*
    *(Answer: **b**.)*

52. *If two-sigma limits are substituted for conventional three-sigma limits on a control chart, one of the following occurs:*
    a. *decrease in alpha risk.*
    b. *increase in beta risk.*
    c. *increase in alpha risk.*
    d. *increase in sample size.*
    (Answer: c.)

53. *In the planning for quality information equipment, an appropriate activity would be to:*
    a. *review present process capabilities to permit correlation with newer processes.*
    b. *establish training plans as required for the operation of the equipment.*
    c. *establish the routine for checkout and calibration tooling.*
    d. *evaluate process cost relative to performance.*
    (Answer: b.)

54. *Good forms design and layout are essential in both manual and electronic data processing because:*
    a. *they are easier to read, check data, use and file.*
    b. *they are cheaper (faster) to use although initial cost is higher than quickly made forms.*
    c. *they help to avoid typographical errors.*
    d. *all of above.*
    (Answer: d.)

55. *The "Least Squares Method" is used in:*
    a. *the Central Limit Theorem.*
    b. *calculating σ^2.*
    c. *calculating σ^2 from σ^2.*

     d. calculating a best fit regression line.
     e. inspecting hole locations.
     (Answer: **d.***)*

56. *A large lot of parts is rejected by your customer and found to be 20%*
     defective. What is the probability that the lot would have been
     accepted by the following sampling plan: sample size = 10; accept if no
     defectives; reject if one or more defectives?
     a. .89
     b. .63
     c. .01
     d. .80
     e. .11
     (Answer: **e.** *This is a Binomial distribution.)*

57. *A correlation problem:*
     a. is solved by estimating the value of the dependent variable for
     various values of the independent variable.
     b. considers the joint variation of two measurements, neither of which
     is restricted by the experimenter.
     c. is the one case where the underlying distributions must be geometric.
     d. is solved by assuming that the variables are normally and
     independently distributed with mean = 0 and variance = σ_e^2.
     (Answer: **b.***)*

58. *In the regression equation y = mx + b, y increases with x in all cases:*
     a. if b is positive.
     b. if b is negative.
     c. if m is positive.
     d. if m is negative.
     (Answer: **c.***)*

59. *A Latin Square design is noted for its straightforward analysis of interaction effects. The above statement is:*
    a. *true in every case.*
    b. *true sometimes depending on the size of the square.*
    c. *true only for Greco-Latin Squares.*
    d. *false in every case.*
    e. *false except for Greco-Latin Squares.*
    (Answer: d.)

60. *When you perform "one experiment" with "forty-nine repetitions," what are the fifty experiments called?*
    a. *randomization.*
    b. *replications.*
    c. *planned grouping.*
    d. *experimental pattern.*
    e. *sequential.*
    (Answer: b.)

61. *In performing an analysis of variance in a single factor experiment, a fundamental assumption which is made is that the:*
    a. *factor (column) means are equal.*
    b. *factor (column) means are unequal.*
    c. *column variances are equal.*
    d. *column variances are significantly different.*
    (Answer: c.)

62. *A factorial experiment has been performed to determine the effect of factor A and factor B on the strength of a part. An "F" test shows a significant interaction effect. This means that:*
    a. *either factor A or factor B has a significant effect on strength.*
    b. *both factor A and factor B effect strength.*
    c. *the effect of changing factor B can be estimated only if the level of factor A is known.*

d. *neither factor A nor factor B effect strength.*

e. *that strength will increase if factor A is increased while factor B is held at 3 low level.*

(Answer: c.)

63. *The purpose of such an experiment described in the previous problem is to compare:*

    a. *the output variances of the three machines.*

    b. *the variance of the machines against the error.*

    c. *the output averages of the three machines.*

    d. *the process capabilities of the three machines.*

    (Answer: c.)

64. *Given the following results obtained from a fixed factor randomized block designed experiment in which the production outputs of three machines A, B, C are compared:*

A	4	8	5	7	6
B	2	0	1	-2	4
C	-3	1	-2	-1	0

    How many degrees of freedom are used to compute the error variance?

    a. *2*

    b. *3*

    c. *12*

    d. *14*

    (Answer: c.)

65. *What is the critical value of F at 0.05 risk for the previous problem?*

    a. *3.89*

    b. *4.75*

    c. *3.49*

    d. *4.60*

    (Answer: a.)

66. *What is the sum of squares for the error term in the previous problem?*
   a. *170*
   b. *130*
   c. *40*
   d. *14*
   (Answer: c.)

67. *An incomplete block design may be especially suitable when:*
   a. *there is missing data.*
   b. *there is need for fractional replication.*
   c. *it may not be possible to apply all treatments in every block.*
   d. *there is need to estimate the parameters during the experimentation.*
   (Answer: c.)

68. *The main objection of designed experimentation in an industrial environment is:*
   a. *obtaining more information for less cost than can be obtained by traditional experimentation.*
   b. *getting excessive scrap as a result of choosing factor levels that are too extreme.*
   c. *verifying that one factor at a time is a most economical way to proceed.*
   d. *obtaining data and then deciding what to do with it.*
   (Answer: b.)

69. *A Latin square design is an experimental design which:*
   a. *cannot be used when an estimation of the interaction effects is desired.*
   b. *affords a good estimate of interaction effects.*
   c. *is useful because the underlying distributions need not be normal.*
   d. *avoids the need to assume that the effects are additive.*
   (Answer: a.)

70. *The basic reason for randomness in sampling is to:*
     a. make certain that the sample represents the population.
     b. eliminate personal bias.
     c. guarantee to reduce the cost of inspection.
     d. guarantee correct lot inferences.
     *(Answer: **b**.)*

71. *To state that the levels of a factor are fixed indicates that:*
     a. the levels are to be set at certain fixed values.
     b. the equipment from which the data are collected must not be moved.
     c. the factors under consideration are qualitative.
     d. the levels were chosen from a finite population.
     *(Answer: **a**.)*

72. *When considering qualitative and quantitative factors in the same designed experiment:*
     a. the sum of squares for the qualitative factors can still be calculated even though no numerical scale can be attached to the levels.
     b. tables of orthogonal polynomials do not apply because no numerical scale can be attached to one of the factors.
     c. the interactions between qualitative and quantitative factors no longer make sense.
     d. the tables of orthogonal polynomials apply to both types of factors if the levels of each are equally spaced.
     *(Answer: **a**.)*

73. *When constructing a factorial experiment, one of the following is true:*
     a. factorial experiments may not contain any number of levels per factor. They must be the same for each factor.
     b. confounding takes place in factorials when we run a fractional part of the complete experiment.

c. contrasts and treatment combinations are the same.
d. in factorials, the factors must be quantitative.
*(Answer: **b**.)*

74.   *The error term $\in_{ij}$ of the population model $\mu_{ij} = \mu + \tau_{ij} + \in_{ij}$ is usually considered:*
      a. normally and independently distributed with mean = 0, variance = 1.
      b. normally and randomly distributed with mean = 0, variance = 1.
      c. randomly distributed with mean = 0, variance = σ_e^2
      d. normally and independently distributed with mean = 0, variance = σ_e^2
      *(Answer: **d**.)*

75.   *A 3^2 experiment indicates:*
      a. two levels of three factors.
      b. three independent variables and two dependent variables.
      c. three-levels of two factors.
      d two go-no-go variables and three continuous variables.
      *(Answer: **c**.)*

76.   *Information generated in a designed experiment:*
      a. always results in an analysis of variance table.
      b. is based on the fact that the variance of the sum is the sum of the variances.
      c. must always be quantitative.
      d. may be based on values which are not necessarily numerical.
      *(Answer: **d**.)*

77.   *When considering a factorial experiment, observe that:*
      a. this experiment cannot be used when complete randomization is necessary.
      b. a main effect may be confounded.

c. this type of design is not encountered often in industrial experiments.
d. one of the advantages is that an exact test always exists for all effects.
(Answer: b.)

78. *The power of efficiency in designed experiments lies in the:*
    a. random order of performance.
    b. the sequential and cyclical procedure of conjecture to design to analysis and back to conjecture.
    c. hidden replication.
    d the large number of possible combinations of factors.
    (Answer: c.)

79. *In the analysis of variance:*
    a. the total sum of squares of deviations from the grand mean is equal to the sum of squares of deviations between treatment means and the grand mean minus the sum of squares of deviations within treatments.
    b. the total standard deviation is equal to the sum of the standard deviation for the treatment effect plus the standard deviation of the random error.
    c. the degrees of freedom are additive.
    d. a basic population model can be constructed to represent the behavior of the experimentation.
    (Answer: c.)

80. *In every experiment there is experimental error. Which one of the following statements is true?*
    a. this error is due to lack of uniformity of the material used in the experiment and to inherent variability in the experimental technique.
    b. this error can be changed statistically by increasing the degrees of freedom.

c. the error can be reduced only by improving the material.
d. in a well-designed experiment there is no interaction effect.
(Answer: **a.**)

81. Random selection of a sample:
   a. theoretically means that each item in the lot had an equal chance to be selected in the sample.
   b. assures that the sample average will equal the population average.
   c. means that a table of random numbers was used to dictate the selection.
   d. is a meaningless theoretical requirement.
   (Answer: **a.**)

82. Consumer risk is defined as:
   a. accepting an unsatisfactory lot a satisfactory.
   b. passing a satisfactory lot a satisfactory.
   c. an alpha risk.
   d. a 5% risk of accepting an unsatisfactory lot.
   (Answer: **a.**)

83. The steeper the OC-curve, the:
   a. less protection for both producer and consumer.
   b. more protection for both producer and consumer.
   c. the lower the AQL.
   d. the smaller the sample size.
   (Answer: **b.** See section III.F Acceptance sampling. Also see question 51, this section.)

84. In MIL-STD-105E, the AQL is always determined at what P on the OC-curve:
   a. 0.05
   b. 0.10
   c. 0.90

d. 0.95
e. none of the above
(Answer: e.)

85. *For an operation requiring shipments from your vendor of small lots of*
    fixed size, the sampling plan used for receiving inspection should have
    its OC curve developed using:
    a. the Poisson distribution
    b. the Hypergeometric distribution
    c. the Binomial distribution
    d. the Log Normal distribution
    e. the Gaussian (normal) distribution
    (Answer: b.)

86. *Two quantities which uniquely determine a single sampling attributes*
    plan are:
    a. AOQL and LTPD.
    b. sample size and rejection number.
    c. AQL and producer's risk.
    d. LTPD and consumer's risk.
    e. AQL and LTPD.
    (Answer: b.)

87. *Selection of a sampling plan from the Dodge-Romig AOQL sampling*
    tables:
    a. requires an estimate of the AOQ.
    b. requires an estimate of the process average.
    c. requires sorting of rejected lots.
    d. requires larger samples than MIL-STD-105E for equivalent quality
       assurance.
    e. requires that we assume a consumer's risk of .05.
    (Answer: b.)

88. *MIL-STD-105E sampling plans allow reduced inspection when four requirements are met. One of these is:*
    a. *inspection level I is specified.*
    b. *10 lots have been on normal inspection and none have been rejected.*
    c. *the process average is less than the AOQL.*
    d. *the maximum percent defective is less than the AQL.*
    e. *all of the above.*
    (Answer: b.)

89. *The AQL for a given sampling plan is 1.0%. This means that:*
    a. *the producer takes a small risk of rejecting product which is 1.0% defective or better.*
    b. *all accepted lots are 1.0% defective or better.*
    c. *the average quality limit of the plan is 1.0%.*
    d. *the average quality level of the plan is 1.0%.*
    e. *all lots are 1.0% defective or better.*
    (Answer: a.)

90. *Considerations to be made prior to the use of any sampling plan is (are):*
    a. *the consumer's and producer's risks must be specified.*
    b. *the method of selecting samples must be specified.*
    c. *the characteristics to be inspected must be specified.*
    d. *the conditions must be specified (material accumulated in lots or inspected by continuous sampling).*
    e. *all of the above.*
    (Answer: e.)

91. *The probability of accepting material produced at an acceptable quality level is defined as:*
    a. α
    b. β
    c. *AQL*

d. $1 - \alpha$

e. $1 - \beta$

(Answer: d.)

92. **AOQL means:**

    a. average outgoing quality level.

    b. average outgoing quality limit.

    c. average outside quality limit.

    d. anticipated optimum quality level.

    (Answer: b.)

93. **Why would inspection by variables be superior to inspection by attributes?**

    a. Inspection by variables is easier to administer than inspection by attributes.

    b. Inspectors like inspection by variables better than inspection by attributes.

    c. More information is obtained when inspection by variables is utilized.

    d Inspection by variables is usually more economical than inspection by attributes.

    e. Inspection by variables makes more sense than inspection by attributes.

    (Answer: c.)

94. **MIL-STD-105E is to be used to select a single sampling plan for lots of 8,000 under normal inspection, Level II, and an AQL of 2.5%. The exact AOQL for the plan is:**

    a. 2.50%

    b. 3.00%

    c. 3.22%

d. 3.30%

e. 2.60%

(Answer: c.)

95. A lot of 50 pieces contains 5 defectives. A sample of two is drawn without replacement. The probability that both will be defective is approximately:

a. .4000

b. .0100

c. .0010

d. .0082

e. .0093

(Answer: d.)

96. You are to construct an OC curve. Which of the following cannot be used as an abscissa value?

a. AOQL.

b. ASN.

c. AQL.

d. LTPD.

e. all of these can be abscissa values.

(Answer: b.)

97. Your major product cannot be fully inspected without destruction. You have been requested to plan the inspection program, including some product testing, in the most cost-effective manner. You most probably will recommend that samples selected for the product verification be based upon:

a. MIL-STD-105E, latest issue; attribute sampling.

b. MIL-STD-414, latest issue; variables sampling.

c. either answers a or b above will meet your criteria.

d. neither answers a nor b above will meet your criteria.

(Answer: b.)

98. The basic concept of *MIL-STD-105E sampling tables and procedures is that:*
    a. poor product is accepted infrequently.
    b. good product is accepted rarely.
    c. poor product is accepted consistently
    d. good product is accepted most of the time.
    (Answer: d.)

99. In acceptance sampling, the probability of accepting a rejectable lot is called:
    a. beta.
    b. AQL.
    c. alpha.
    d. LTPD.
    (Answer: a.)

100. The Dodge-Romig sampling tables for AOQL protection:
    a. require sorting of rejected lots.
    b. are the same in principle as the MIL-STD-105E tables.
    c. do not depend upon the process average.
    d require larger samples than MIL-STD-105E for equivalent quality assurances.
    (Answer: a.)

101. A cost estimate associated with average outgoing quality protection is usually determined from the:
    a. average total inspection.
    b. average outgoing quality.
    c. average sample size.
    d. acceptable quality limit.
    (Answer: a.)

102. Using a 10 percent sample of each lot, with an acceptance number of zero, regardless of lot size:
   a. results in a constant level of protection against bad product.
   b. assures a constant producer's risk.
   c. abdicates the responsibility for pre-determining quality requirements.
   d. provides an AQL of zero and an LTPD of 10 percent.
   (Answer: c.)

103. The operating characteristic (OC) curve of an acceptance sampling plan:
   a. demonstrates how the plan will reject all of the lots worse than the AQL.
   b. shows the ability of the plan to distinguish between good and bad lots.
   c. shows the relative cost of sampling for various levels of quality.
   d. demonstrates the advantages of double sampling over single sampling.
   (Answer: b.)

104. The Dodge-Romig tables for AOQL protection are designed to provide:
   a. minimum average sampling costs.
   b. maximum protection against poor material.
   c. maximum risk of accepting good lots.
   d. minimum average total inspection for a given process average.
   (Answer: d.)

105. To achieve consistent lot-by-lot protection the receiving inspector should
   a. allow no defective product into the shop.
   b. return all rejected lots to the vendor.
   c. not know how the vendor inspects the product.
   d. use a sampling plan based on LTPD.
   (Answer: d.)

106. *100 percent inspection is:*
    a. used to sort items.
    b. at best only 60 percent effective.
    c. assures a satisfactory outgoing quality level.
    d. is theoretically unsound but is an excellent practice.
    (Answer: a.)

107. *The two factors that have the most to do with determining an attributes sampling plan (assuming a binomial distribution) are:*
    a. sample size and rejection number.
    b. lot size and sample size.
    c. lot size and acceptance number.
    d. none of above.
    (Answer: a.)

108. *Double sampling is better than single sampling because:*
    a. it involves less inspection regardless of lot quality.
    b. if the first sample rejects the lot the second sample will accept it.
    c. it is more economical except when lots are of borderline quality.
    d. it is easier to administer.
    (Answer: c.)

♦ ♦ ♦
CHAPTER

IV

Product, Process, and Materials Control

A. SOLUTIONS TO SELECTED EXERCISES FOUND IN THE COMPLETE GUIDE TO THE CQE

1. *Explain the difference between the terms defect and defective.*

   See Appendix Table 4.

   (See section IV.B Classification of characteristics)

2. *What is the primary reason for establishing lot traceability?*

   Safety.

   (See section IV.D Lot traceability)

3. *What are the typical responsibilities of a MRB?*

   Disposition of non-conforming materials (e.g., scrap, rework, down-grade); approval of rework and reinspection plans; evaluation and follow up of corrective action plans.

   (See section IV.E Materials segregation practices)

4. *Name four types of samples and provide one or more examples of each.*

   Acceptance sample, SPC sample, process validation sample, measurement system correlation sample. Examples should be evaluated

by referencing the definitions of each sample type provided in the text.
(See section IV.G Sample integrity and control)

5. *What are the basic properties of a distribution?*
    Central tendency, spread and shape.
    (See section IV.H Statistical process control)

6. *What are the four main elements of a process feedback system?*
    The process itself, information about the state of the process while
    certain outcomes were generated, action taken on the process, action
    taken on output from the process.
    (See section IV.H Statistical process control)

7. *The text described a process of more than one person writing the letter
    "a" several times. Identify at least ten sources of variation in this process
    and classify each as either a special cause or a common cause.*
    (See section IV.H Statistical process control)

8. *The general manager is concerned about quality. As part of her quality
    improvement initiative she has informed all department managers that
    they should have daily meetings to study every defective item returned
    by customers to identify the cause of the problem. A control chart of
    customer returns indicates statistical control. Is the general manager's
    plan likely to be effective? If not, why not?*
    No. The manager's plan is essentially problem solving. The implica-
    tion of her approach is that the process itself is adequate, but that
    "problems" are creating defective items. However, the control chart
    indicates a stable process, albeit an unacceptable process. In other
    words, there is no "problem" per se. The process itself is the problem
    and it is the process that should be studied, not the defective items it
    produces. The manager's approach is almost certain to result in
    tampering, which will make matters worse.
    (See section IV.H Statistical process control)

9.   *Determine the correct chart for the following:*
   a. waiting time for customers in a bank, each individual customer's waiting time will be plotted;
   b. the salt content of potato chips using samples of three every 15 minutes;
   c. the thickness of ceramic substrates using samples of 10 from each batch produced;
   d. the number of customers who complain per 100 customers served;
   e. the proportion of customers served each day who complain;
   f. the number of falls in the hospital reported each week;
   g. the number of medication order errors per day.
   a. X chart;
   b. X-bar and R or X-bar and s;
   c. X bar and s;
   d. np chart;
   e. p chart;
   f. c chart;
   g. u chart.
   (See section IV. H Statistical process control)

10.   *Based on subgroups of n=5 the grand average is 105 and the average range is 10. Compute the upper and lower control limits for the X-bar and R charts.*
   Range chart: LCL = 0, UCL = 2.114 * 10 = 21.14.
   Averages: LCL = 99.23, UCL = 110.77.
   (See section IV.H Statistical process control)

11.   *Based on subgroups of n=15 the grand average is 10 and the average subgroup sigma is 0.5. Compute the upper and lower control limits for the X-bar and s charts.*
   Sigma chart: LCL = 0.2140, UCL = 0.7860.
   Averages: LCL = 9.6055, UCL = 10.3945.
   (See section IV.H Statistical process control)

12. *The average hospital census over the past 24 months has been stable at 68 patients. The average variation month-to-month is 6 patients and it is also stable. The most recent census is 80 patients, is the process still in statistical control?*

LCL = 52.04, UCL = 83.96. Since 80 is within these limits, the answer is yes, the process is in statistical control.

(See section IV.H Statistical process control)

13. *Construct a p chart using the following data:*

MONTH	IV LINES	INFECTIONS	%
Nov-92	29	1	3.4%
Dec-92	28	1	3.6%
Jan-93	37	4	10.8%
Feb-93	27	0	0.0%
Mar-93	26	1	3.8%
Apr-93	29	2	6.9%
May-93	22	1	4.5%
Jun-93	25	1	4.0%
Jul-93	32	0	0.0%
Aug-93	41	1	2.4%
Sep-93	38	2	5.3%
Oct-93	33	0	0.0%

Solution

MONTH	IV Lines	INFECTIONS	%	LCL	Avg. %	UCL
Nov-92	29	1	3.4%	0.0%	3.8%	14.5%
Dec-92	28	1	3.6%	0.0%	3.8%	14.7%
Jan-93	37	4	10.8%	0.0%	3.8%	13.3%
Feb-93	27	0	0.0%	0.0%	3.8%	14.9%
Mar-93	26	1	3.8%	0.0%	3.8%	15.1%
Apr-93	29	2	6.9%	0.0%	3.8%	14.5%
May-93	22	1	4.5%	0.0%	3.8%	16.1%
Jun-93	25	1	4.0%	0.0%	3.8%	15.3%
Jul-93	32	0	0.0%	0.0%	3.8%	14.0%
Aug-93	41	1	2.4%	0.0%	3.8%	12.8%
Sep-93	38	2	5.3%	0.0%	3.8%	13.1%
Oct-93	33	0	0.0%	0.0%	3.8%	13.8%
TOTALS	367	14				

(See section IV.H Statistical process control)

14. *The inspector samples 100 can ends per subgroup and records the number of can ends with coating defects. The average number of defective ends is 25. Compute the upper and lower control limits for the appropriate control chart.*

Either the p chart or the np chart is correct.

If np chart is selected: LCL = 12.00, UCL = 37.99

If p chart is selected: LCL = 0.12, UCL = 0.38.

(See section IV.H Statistical process control)

15. *In a typical week a large factory has 16 accidents. Find the upper and lower control limits for the number of accidents per week.*

The correct chart is a c chart. LCL = 4, UCL = 28.

(See section IV.H Statistical process control)

16. *In a typical week a large factory has 16 accidents. Find the upper and lower control limits for plotting the number of accidents per month and per 13-week quarter.*

    The correct chart is a U chart.

    There are four weeks in a month so n=4. Thus, for monthly plotted points: LCL = 10, UCL = 22

    For a 13 week quarter: LCL = 12.67, UCL = 19.33.

    (See section IV.H Statistical process control)

17. *Discuss the key differences between random sampling and rational subgroup sampling.*

    (See section IV.H.3.c Rational subgroup sampling)

18. *Find a real-world example of each of the four funnel rules discussed in IV.H.3.f.*

    (See section IV.H.3.f Tampering effects and diagnosis)

19. *A stable process has a mean of 53 and an average range of 4, using subgroups of n=4. The requirements are 50±8. Compute each of the indices shown in Table IV.9. Estimate the percentage low and high and discuss the capability of this process.*

$$\hat{\sigma} = \frac{\overline{R}}{d_2} = \frac{4}{2.059} = 1.94$$

$$C_P = \frac{16}{6 \times 1.94} = 1.37$$

$$C_R = 100 \times \frac{6 \times 1.94}{16} = 72.75\%$$

$$C_M = \frac{16}{8 \times 1.94} = 1.03$$

$$Z_U = \frac{58 - 53}{1.94} = 2.58$$

$$Z_L = \frac{53 - 42}{1.94} = 5.67$$

$$Z_{MIN} = 2.58$$

$$C_{PK} = \frac{2.58}{3} = 0.86$$

$$C_{PM} = \frac{1.37}{\sqrt{1 + \frac{(53-50)^2}{1.94^2}}} = \frac{1.37}{1.84} = 0.74$$

Estimated below the low specification: 0%

Estimated above the high specification: 0.49%.

The Cp and Cr statistics indicate that this process has a small enough spread to meet the requirements. However, Cpk and Cpm indicate that the process is not meeting the requirements. The conclusion is that the process is off-center. Evaluating the Zu and Z_L statistics show that the process is offset to the high side, since Zu < Z_L. If the process were centered then Cpk = Cp = 1.37 and the requirements are 3 x 1.37 = 4.11 standard deviations away from the mean. At this level the estimated process defectives would be in the ppm range.

Cm indicates that if this is a machine capability study rather than a process capability study the performance is only marginal. Additional variation from operators, materials, etc. could well lead to problems.

(See section IV.H Statistical process control)

B. DETAILED SOLUTIONS TO SELECTED PAST EXAM QUESTIONS

1. *A technique whereby various product features are graded as to relative importance is called*
   a. classification of defects.
   b. quality engineering.
   c. classification of characteristics.
   d. feature grading.

   The question describes classification of characteristics, choice *c*. This is an essential activity whose purpose is to separate the vital few characteristics from the trivial many so that an effective allocation of resources is possible. Classification of defects is also quite common. The prospective CQE should be familiar with the defect classifications in MIL-STD-105E.
   (See section IV.B Classification of characteristics)

2. *One of the major hazards in the Material Review Board procedure is the tendency of the board to emphasize only the disposition function and to neglect the _____ _____ function.*
   a. statistical analysis
   b. corrective action
   c. material evaluation
   d. tolerance review
   e. manufacturing methods

   The tendency of MRB's to underemphasize corrective action is both well known and unfortunate. Choice *b* is correct.
   (See section IV.F Materials review board criteria and procedures)

3. *An $\overline{X}$ and R chart was prepared for an operation using twenty samples with five pieces in each sample. $\overline{\overline{X}}$ was found to be 33.6 and $\overline{R}$ was 6.20. During production a sample of five was taken and the pieces measured 36, 43, 37, 25, and 38. At the time this sample was taken:*

   a. both average and range were within control limits.

   b. neither average nor range were within control limits.

   c. only the average was outside control limits.

   d. only the range was outside control limits.

   We find the control limits are

   Range Chart

   $$LCL_R = D_3\overline{R} = (0)(6.2) = 0$$

   $$UCL_R = D_4\overline{R} = (2.114)(6.2) = 13.1$$

   Averages Chart

   $$LCL_{\overline{X}} = \overline{\overline{X}} - A_2\overline{R} = 33.6 - .577 \times 6.2 = 30.0$$

   $$LCL_{\overline{X}} = \overline{\overline{X}} + A_2\overline{R} = 33.6 + .577 \times 6.2 = 37.2$$

For the 5 piece sample

   $\overline{X} = 35.8$

   R = 18

Thus $\overline{X}$ is in control, R is not; choice *d.*

(See section IV.H.2 Types of control charts)

4. *An electronics firm was experiencing high rejections in their multiple connector manufacturing departments. "P" charts were introduced as part of a program to reduce defectives. Control limits were based on prior history, using the formula:*

$$P' \pm 3\sqrt{\frac{P'(100-P')}{N}}$$

P' is the historical value of percent defective and N is the number of pieces inspected each week. After six weeks, the following record was accumulated.

Dept.	P'	Week 1	Week 2	Week 3	Week 4	Week 5	Week 6
104	9	8	11	6	13	12	10
105	16	13	19	20	12	15	17
106	15	18	19	16	11	13	16

1000 pieces were inspected each week in each department. Which department(s) exhibited a point or points out of control during this period? (Round off calculations to nearest tenth of a percentage point.)
a. Department 104
b. Department 105
c. Department 106
d. All of the departments
e. None of the departments

The control limits for the three departments are
Dept 104

$$LCL_p = 9 - 3\sqrt{\frac{9(100-9)}{1000}} = 6.3\%$$

$$UCL_p = 9 + 3\sqrt{\frac{9(100-9)}{1000}} = 11.7\%$$

Dept 105

$$LCL_p = 16 - 3\sqrt{\frac{16(100-16)}{1000}} = 12.5\%$$

$$UCL_p = 16 + 3\sqrt{\frac{16(100-16)}{1000}} = 19.5\%$$

Dept 106

$$LCL_p = 15 - 3\sqrt{\frac{15(100-15)}{1000}} = 11.6\%$$

$$UCL_p = 15 + 3\sqrt{\frac{15(100-15)}{1000}} = 18.4\%$$

When these are compared to the data given we find

Dept. 104:   Below LCL_p at week 3

Above UCL_p at weeks 4 and 5

Dept. 105:   Below LCL_p at week 4

Above UCL_p at week 3

Dept. 106:   Below LCL_p at week 4

Above UCL_p at week 2

Thus choice *d* is correct.

(See section IV.H.2.b Attribute charts)

5. *A process is checked by inspection of random samples of four shafts after a polishing operation, and $\overline{X}$ and R charts are maintained. A person making a spot check picks out two shafts, measures them accurately, and plots the value of each on the $\overline{X}$ chart. Both points fall just outside the control limits. He advises the department foreman to stop the process. This decision indicates that*

a. the process level is out of control.

b. both the level and dispersion are out of control.

c. the process level is out of control but not the dispersion.

d. the person is not using the chart correctly.

The person plotted individual readings on a chart for averages. Also, he only sampled 2 items instead of 4. He is not using the chart correctly, choice *d*.

(See section IV.H.2 Types of control charts)

6. *When used together for variables data, which of the following pair of quantities is the most useful in preparing control charts?*

a. AQL, p'

b. p, n

c. $\overline{X}$, R

d. R, σ

The best choice is *c*. Choices *a* and *b* refer to attributes data quality measures. Both the values in choice *d* refer to measures of *dispersion*. Only choice *c* can measure both central tendency and dispersion for a process.

(See section IV.H.2 Types of control charts)

7. *The following measurements for a sample with Dimension X are representative of a process known to be in statistical control.*

42, 52, 64, 45, 53, 56, 70, 57, 49, 62

Which of the following best approximates the upper and lower control limits of the process capability? (Use generally accepted sigma limits for the United States.)

a. 81 & 29

b. 59 & 51

c. 64 & 46

d. 70 & 42

When n = 10 the process capability of 6σ can be approximated as 2R. This set of data yields the following

$\overline{X}$= 55

R = 70 − 42 = 28

Thus the limits are
    Lower Limit = 55 − 28 = 27
    Upper Limit = 55 + 28 = 83
This gives choice *a* as the closest, which is correct.
(See section IV.H.4 Process capability studies and indices)

8. *A process is in control at* $\overline{\overline{X}}$ *= 100,* $\overline{R}$ *= 7.3 with n = 4. If the process level shifts to 101.5, with the same* $\overline{R}$ *, what is the probability that the next* $\overline{X}$ *point will fall outside the old control limits?*
    a. .016
    b. .029
    c. .122
    d. .360

    Since sample means are normally distributed we will use normal tables to get the probability. We must compute Z to enter these tables, where

$$Z = \frac{Limit - \overline{\overline{X}}}{\sigma/\sqrt{n}}$$

For a controlled process we can use the estimate of σ

$$\hat{\sigma} = \overline{R}/d_2$$

We find d_2 in a table of factors for control charts at n = 4 is d_2 = 2.059. Thus

$$\hat{\sigma} = 7.3/2.059 = 3.56$$

If the shift in $\overline{\overline{X}}$ is upward then the probability of an $\overline{X}$ being below the lower limit is negligible. Thus we will only consider the probability of exceeding an upper limit. Before the shift our upper control limit (UCL) was

$$UCL = \overline{\overline{X}} + A_2\overline{R}$$

where A_2 is obtained from control chart factor tables at n = 4 as .729.

Thus UCL = 100 + .729 (7.3) = 105.3217 ≅ 105.3
This gives

$$Z = \frac{105.3 - 101.5}{3.56 / \sqrt{4}} = 2.13$$

Using normal tables we find
Prob ($\overline{X}$ > 105.3) = Prob (Z > 2.13) = .016
Choice *a*.
(See section IV.H.4 Process capability studies and indices. See also III.B Distributions)

9. *The spread of individual observations from a normal process capability distribution may be expressed numerically as*
   a. $6\overline{R}/d_2$
   b. $2 \times A_2 \overline{R}$
   c. $\overline{R}/d_2$
   d. $D_4 \overline{R}$

   If and only if a process is in control then the standard deviation can be estimated from the average range by the equation s = $\overline{R}$/d2 where
   s = Standard deviation
   $\overline{R}$ = The average range
   d_2 = A table factor that depends on the sample size.
In quality control we often estimate the capability of a normally distributed process to be 6s, as illustrated below.

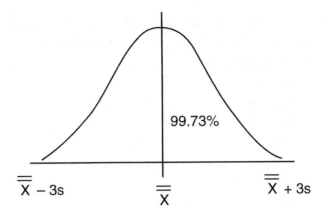

$$\overline{\overline{X}} - 3s \qquad\qquad \overline{\overline{X}} \qquad\qquad \overline{\overline{X}} + 3s$$

Thus the correct answer is *a*.
(See section IV.H.4 Process capability studies and indices)

10. **Which one of the following best describes machine capability?**
    a. the total variation of all cavities of a mold, cavities of a die cast machine or spindles of an automatic assembly machine.
    b. the inherent variation of the machine.
    c. the total variation over a shift.
    d. the variation in a short run of consecutively produced parts.

    Choice *b* is best. *Inherent* variability is the variation that remains after all *assignable* causes of variation have been eliminated. It is often called *random variation.*
    (See section IV.H.4 Process capability studies and indices)

11. *Machine capability studies on four machines yielded the following information:*

Machine	Average ($\overline{X}$)	Capability (6σ)
#1	1.495	.004"
#2	1.502	.006"
#3	1.500	.012"
#4	1.498	.012"

(11.) *The tolerance on the particular dimension is 1.500± .005". If the average value can be readily shifted by adjustment to the machine, then the* **best** *machine to use is:*
a. *Machine #1.*
b. *Machine #2.*
c. *Machine #3.*
d. *Machine #4.*

Since we can, by assumption, shift the average value, the $\overline{X}$ column can be ignored. Thus the best choice is the machine with the least dispersion, which is machine #1.
(See section IV.H.4 Process capability studies and indices)

12. *Based on the information given in the above question, if the average value cannot be readily shifted by adjustment to the machine and no rework or repair is possible, then the* **best** *machine to use is*
a. *Machine #1.*
b. *Machine #2.*
c. *Machine #3.*
d. *Machine #4.*

We now seek the machine which gives the smallest proportion discrepant. If we assume a normal distribution for each machine, the answer will be found using the Z statistics for each machine, namely

$$Z_U = \frac{\text{upper specification} - \overline{\overline{X}}}{\hat{\sigma}}$$

This gives

Machine	Zlow spec	Z high spec
#1	0	+15.0
#2	-7.0	+3.0
#3	-2.5	+2.5
#4	-1.5	+3.5

A casual glance through the normal tables (Appendix Table 5) (which is all you'll have time for in the real CQE exam) will show that machine #2 is easily the best choice.

(See section IV.H.4 Process capability studies and indices)

C. SIMULATED EXAM QUESTIONS

1. *To demonstrate compliance to a requirement that the Cpk index be at least 1.33 based on a ±3σ spread, the quality engineer computed Cpk from fifty units selected at random from the production lot before it was delivered to the customer. Which of the following statements describes this approach to capability analysis?*
    a. it is invalid because no rational subgroup was used.
    b. it is an acceptable method of computing Cpk.
    c. it is invalid because the process may be out of control, which would not be detected with this approach.
    d. it is invalid because the estimate of σ is based on within-subgroup variation only.
    e. All of the above except b.

    The correct answer is *e*. Few methods have suffered from more abuse in recent years that capability analysis. Many large companies have mandated SPC, complete with capability analysis, of all key suppliers. The contractual requirements have been enforced at times by auditors who apparently don't have a good grasp of the underlying assumptions involved. The CQE should strive to understand all of the subtleties of capability analysis.

    More recently, the Cpm index, sometimes called the Taguchi capability index, has been enjoying popularity. Like Cpk, the Cpm index accounts for both the process central tendency and its spread. However, Cpm works with a target value, while Cpk is based on the nearest tolerance limit. Cpm also has certain mathematical advantages over Cpk, such as a known probability distribution.

    (See section IV.H.4 Process capability studies and indices)

D. ANSWERS TO SELECTED PAST EXAM QUESTIONS

1. *The inspection plan for a new product line may include*
   a. *detailed production schedule.*
   b. *sampling procedures and techniques.*
   c. *internal techniques for control and segregation of conforming or nonconforming product.*
   d. *answers a and b above.*
   e. *answers a, b, and c above.*
   (Answer: e.)

2. *Classification of defects is most essential as a prior step to a valid establishment of:*
   a. *design characteristics to be inspected.*
   b. *vendor specifications of critical parts.*
   c. *process control points.*
   d. *economical sampling inspection.*
   e. *a product audit check list.*
   (Answer: d.)

3. *"Beauty Defects" can best be described for Inspection acceptance purposes by:*
   a. *simply stating such defects are unacceptable.*
   b. *verbally describing rejection criteria.*
   c. *leaving them up to the inspector.*
   d. *establishing visual standards and/or samples describing the defects.*
   e. *establishing written standards describing the defects.*
   (Answer: d.)

4. *Classification of characteristics:*
   a. *is the same as classification of defects.*
   b. *can only be performed after product is produced.*

c. must have tolerances associated with it.

d. is independent of defects.

(Answer: d. See section IV.B Classification of characteristics and Appendix Table 4.)

5. *Characteristics are often classified (critical, major, etc.) so that:*

    a. equal emphasis can be placed on each characteristic.

    b. punitive action against the responsible individuals can be equitably distributed.

    c. an assessment of quality can be made.

    d. a quality audit is compatible with management desires.

    (Answer: c. See section IV.B Classification of characteristics)

6. *A classification of characteristics makes it possible to:*

    a. separate the "vital few" from the "trivial many" kinds of defects.

    b. direct the greatest inspection effort to the most important quality characteristics.

    c. establish inspection tolerances.

    d. allow the inspector to choose what to inspect and what not to inspect.

    (Answer: b. See section IV.B Classification of characteristics)

7. *One defective is:*

    a. an item that is unacceptable to the inspector.

    b. the same as one defect

    c. a characteristic that may be unacceptable for more than one reason.

    d. an item that fails to meet quality standards and specifications.

    (Answer: d. See section IV.B Classification of characteristics and Appendix Table 4.)

8. *The primary reason that nonconforming material should be identified and segregated is:*

   a. so that the cause of nonconformity can be determined.

   b. to provide statistical information for the "zero defects" program.

   c. so it cannot be used in production without proper authorization.

   d. to obtain samples of poor workmanship for use in the company's training program.

   e. so that responsibility can be determined and disciplinary action taken.

   (Answer: c.)

9. *In recent months, several quality problems have resulted from apparent change in design specifications by engineering, including material substitutions. This has only come to light through Quality Engineering's failure analysis system. You recommend which of the following quality system provisions as the best corrective action:*

   a. establishing a formal procedure for initial design review.

   b. establishing a formal procedure for process control.

   c. establishing a formal procedure for specification change control (sometimes called an ECO or SCO system).

   d. establishing a formal system for drawing and print control.

   e. establishing a formal material review (MRB) system.

   (Answer: c.)

10. *One of the major hazards in the material review board procedure is the tendency of the board to emphasize only the disposition function and to neglect the _____ _____ function.*

    a. statistical analysis

    b. corrective action

    c. material evaluation

    d. tolerance review

    e. manufacturing methods

    (Answer: b.)

11. *The factor D_4 used in $\overline{X}$ and R control charts is: (UCL = $D_4 \overline{R}$)*
   a. *the distance between the mean and the upper control limit of a range chart.*
   b. *the number of detects in a second sample.*
   c. *the constant which corrects the bias in estimating the population standard deviation from the average range of randomly drawn samples.*
   d. *the probability that $\overline{X}$ is in control.*
   (Answer: a.)

12. *When used together for variables data, which of the following is the most useful pair of quantities in Quality Control?*
   a. *$\overline{X}$, R*
   b. *$\overline{X}$, η*
   c. *R, σ*
   d. *$\overline{p}$, η*
   e. *AQL, p'*
   (Answer: a.)

13. *In control chart theory, the distribution of the number of defects per unit follows very closely the:*
   a. *normal distribution.*
   b. *binomial distribution.*
   c. *Chi-square distribution.*
   d. *Poisson distribution.*
   (Answer: d.)

14. *An electronics firm was experiencing high rejections in their multiple connector manufacturing departments. "P" Charts were introduced as part of a program to reduce defectives. Control limits were based on prior history, using the formula:*

$$P' \pm 3\sqrt{\frac{P'(100 - P')}{N}}$$

Where P' is the historical value of percent defective and N is the number of pieces inspected each week. After six weeks the following record was accumulated:

Percent defective.

Dept.	P'	Week 1	Week 2	Week 3	Week 4	Week 5	Week 6
101	12	11	11	14	15	10	12
102	17	20	17	21	21	20	13
103	22	18	26	27	17	20	19
104	9	8	11	6	13	12	10
105	16	13	19	20	12	15	17
106	15	18	19	16	11	13	16

600 pieces were inspected each week in each department. Which department(s) exhibited a point or points out of control during the period?

a. dept. 101
b. dept. 102
c. dept. 103
d. dept. 104
e. dept. 105

(Answer: d. See section IV.H.2 Types of control charts. Also see question 4 in section B of this chapter.)

15. An $\overline{X}$ and R chart was prepared for an operation using twenty samples with five pieces in each sample. $\overline{X}$ was found to be 33.6 and R was 6.2. During production a sample of five was taken and the pieces measured 36, 43, 37, 34 and 38. At the time this sample was taken:
    a. both average and range were within control limits.
    b. neither average nor range was within control limits.
    c. only the average was outside control limits.
    d. only the range was outside control limits.
    e. the information given is not sufficient to construct an $\overline{X}$ and R chart using tables usually available.
    (Answer: c.)

16. When small samples are used to estimate the standard deviation through use of the range statistic, sample subgroup sizes larger than 20 should not be used because:
    a. the number 20 causes calculation difficulties.
    b. the efficiency of the range as an estimator of the standard deviation falls to 70%.
    c. the distribution for n = 20 is skewed.
    d. n = 20 adversely affects the location of the mean .
    e. the variance is a biased estimate.
    (Answer: b.)

17. A chart for number of defects is called:
    a. np chart.
    b. p chart.
    c. $\overline{X}$ chart.
    d. c chart.
    (Answer: d.)

18. *Using the range method calculate the machine capability standard deviation to nearest 0.0001 of the following:*

8 A.M.	9 A.M.	10 A M	11 A.M.
0.001	0.003	0.001	0.005
-0.001	0.004	-0.002	0.006
0.003	0.003	-0.003	0.005
0.002	0.004	0.002	0.005
0.001	0.002	0.000	0.006

a. *0.0024*

b. *0.0470*

c. *0.0013*

d. *0.0030*

(Answer: c. See section IV.H.2 Types of control charts, see also IV.H.4 Process capability studies and indices)

19. *A process is checked at random by inspection of samples of four shafts after a polishing operation, and $\overline{X}$ and R charts are maintained. A person making a spot check measures two shafts accurately, and plots their range on the R chart. The point falls just outside the control limit. He advises the department foreman to stop the process. This decision indicates that:*

a. *the process level is out of control.*

b. *the process level is out of control but not the dispersion.*

c. *the person is misusing the chart*

d. *the process dispersion is out of control.*

(Answer: d.)

20. *A process is in control with $\overline{p} = 0.10$ and n = 100. The three-sigma limits of the np-control chart are:*

a. *1 and 19*

b. *9.1 and 10.9*

c. 0.01 and 0.19

d. 0.07 and 0.13

(Answer: *a*. See section IV.H.2.b Attribute charts)

21. A "p" chart

a. *can be used for only one type of detect per chart.*

b. *plots the number of defects in a sample.*

c. *plots either the fraction or percent detective in order of time.*

d. *plots variations in dimensions.*

(Answer: *c*. See section IV.H.2.b Attribute charts)

22. *The control chart that is most sensitive to variations in a measurement is:*

a. *p chart*

b. *pn chart.*

c. *c chart*

d. *$\overline{X}$ and R chart.*

(Answer: *d*. See section IV.H.2.b Attribute charts)

23. *The assumed probability distribution for the control chart for number of defects is the:*

a. *Binomial distribution.*

b. *Poisson distribution.*

c. *Normal distribution.*

d. *Student's "t" distribution.*

(Answer: *b*. See section IV.H.2.b Attribute charts)

24. *A p-chart is a type of control chart for:*

a. *plotting bar-stock lengths from receiving inspection samples.*

b. *plotting fraction defective results from shipping inspection samples.*

c. *plotting defects per unit from in-process inspection samples.*

d. answers a, b, and c above.
e. answers a and c only.
*(Answer: **b**. See section IV.H.2.b Attribute charts)*

25. *The sensitivity of a p-chart to changes in quality is:*
   a. equal to that of a range chart.
   b. equal to that of a chart for averages.
   c. equal to that of a c-chart.
   d. equal to that of a u-chart.
   e. none of the above.
   *(Answer: **e**. See section IV.H.2.b Attribute charts)*

26. *A p-chart has exhibited statistical control over a period of time. However the average fraction defective is too high to be satisfactory. Improvement can he obtained by:*
   a. a change in the basic design of the product.
   b. instituting 100% inspection.
   c. a change in the production process through substitution of new tooling or machinery.
   d. all of the above answers are correct except b.
   e. all of the above answers are correct except c.
   *(Answer: **d**. Author's note: this response is debatable.)*

27. *Each value below is the number of defects found in a group of five subassemblies inspected.*

77	61	59	22	54
64	49	54	92	22
75	65	41	89	49
93	45	87	55	33
45	77	40	25	20

   Assume that a c chart is to be used for future production. Calculate the preliminary three-sigma control limits from the above data:

a. *82.5, 28.9*
b. *15.6, 6.6*
c. *65.7, 45.7*
d. *78.2, 33.2*
(Answer: d.)

28. *Referring to the data in the preceding question, if points are outside of the control limits and we wish to set up a control chart for future production:*

   a. *more data are needed.*

   b. *discard those points falling outside the control limits, for which you can identify an assignable cause, and revise the limits.*

   c. *check with production to determine the true process capability.*

   d. *discard those points falling outside the control limits and revise the limits.*

   (Answer: b.)

29. *You have just returned from a two-week vacation and are going over with your QC manager, the control charts which have been maintained during your absence. He calls your attention to the fact that one of the X-charts shows the last 50 points to be very near the centerline. In fact, they all seem to be within about one sigma of the center line. What explanation would you offer him?*

   a. *Somebody "goofed" in the original calculation of the control limits.*

   b. *The process standard deviation has decreased during the time the last 50 samples were taken and nobody thought to recompute the control limits.*

   c. *This is a terrible situation. I'll get on it right away and see what the trouble is. I hope we haven't produced too much scrap.*

   d. *This is fine. The closer the points are to the center line the better our control.*

   (Answer: b. See section IV.H.3.e Rules for determining statistical control.)

30. When an initial study is made of a repetitive industrial process for the purpose of setting up a Shewhart control chart, information on the following process characteristic is sought.
a. process capability.
b. process performance.
c. process reliability.
d. process conformance.
(Answer: a.)

31. On the production floor, parts being produced measure .992 – 1.011. The specification requires the parts to be .995 – 1.005. Which of the following techniques would not be particularly useful in trying to improve and control the process?
a. pre-control.
b. MIL-STD-105 charts.
c. Multi-vari charts.
d. $\overline{X}$ and R charts.
e. machine capability analysis.
(Answer: b. See section III.F Acceptance sampling. The key word in the question is not.)

32. In which one of the following is the use of an $\overline{X}$ and R chart liable to be helpful as a tool to control a process?
a. the machine capability is wider than the specification.
b. the machine capability is equal to the specification.
c. the machine capability is somewhat smaller than the specification.
d. the machine capability is very small compared to the specification.
(Answer: c.)

33. *Which one of the following would most closely describe machine process capability?*
     a. the process variation.
     b. the total variation over a shift.
     c. the total variation of all cavities of a mold, cavities of a die cast machine or spindles of an automatic assembly machine.
     d. the variation in a very short run of consecutively produced parts.
     (Answer: d. See section IV.H.3.c Rational subgroup sampling.)

34. *Recognizing the nature of process variability, the process capability target is usually:*
     a. looser than product specifications.
     b. the same as product specifications.
     c. tighter than product specifications.
     d. not related to product specifications.
     (Answer: c.)

CHAPTER

V

Measurement Systems

A. SOLUTIONS TO SELECTED EXERCISES FOUND IN *THE COMPLETE GUIDE TO THE CQE*

1. *The quality engineer performed a study comparing one micrometer to one caliper. Based on his study he issued a report stating that micrometers were superior to calipers. What is the primary flaw in the engineer's approach?*

    The primary problem (there are *many* secondary problems with this example) is that the study lacks *validity*, specifically, external validity. If the intent is to make a generalization to the universe of all micrometers and calipers, the approach used is simply wrong. The problem lies with trying to represent a large and diverse universe with a single item.
    (See section V.A Terms and definitions)

2. *Explain the relationship between bias and linearity.*

    Bias is a measure of inaccuracy at a point. Linearity is an evaluation of bias at several points over a range of concern.
    (See section V.A Terms and definitions)

3. *What is the interpretation of a National standard?*

    A National standard sits at the top of the hierarchy of standards and it is universally accepted as "true." E.g., the meter standard maintained by NIST is *the* meter by definition.
    (See section V.B.1 Traceability to standards)

4. *Pick a measurement process familiar to you and prepare a cause-and-effect diagram of the causes of measurement error for that process. The branches on the cause-and-effect diagram should be labeled accuracy, repeatability, reproducibility, stability and linearity.*
    (See section V.A Terms and definitions)

5. *What aspect of measurement error is addressed by calibration?*

    Accuracy is the primary area addressed, although other areas might also be affected by properly maintaining the gage.
    (See section V.B.3 Calibration systems)

6. *What was the most popular calibration standard in use in 1996?*
    Mil-Std-45662.
    (See section V.B.3 Calibration systems)

7. *A stable process has a standard deviation of 0.06 on a pH scale. The engineering requirement for pH is 6.2 - 6.6. What is the minimum acceptable gage resolution for this process?*
    0.072

    The measurement system should be able to divided the region of interest into at least five data categories. The region of interest is the smaller of 6 sigma or the tolerance. Since this process is capable, 6 sigma is the region of interest.
    (See section V.C Repeatability and reproducibility studies)

8. *A stable process has a standard deviation of 0.06 on a pH scale. The engineering requirement for pH is 6.4 – 6.6. What is the minimum acceptable gage resolution for this process?*

    0.04

    The measurement system should be able to divided the region of interest into at least five data categories. The region of interest is the smaller of 6 sigma or the tolerance. Since this process is not capable, the tolerance is the region of interest.

    (See section V.C Repeatability and reproducibility studies)

9. *How does inadequate resolution appear on a control chart?*

    Highly stratified, especially on the R chart or X chart. The X-bar chart is less effected because averaging leads to additional decimal places, thus masking the stratification.

    (See section V.C Repeatability and reproducibility studies)

10. *Evaluate accuracy using the following data: reference value = 1.000 inches, average measurement = 1.0007 inches. The measurement system is intended for use on a part with a tolerance of 0.005 inches.*

    bias = 0.0007 inches. % bias = 14%.

    (See section V.C Repeatability and reproducibility studies)

11. *A control chart has been created as follows: thirty parts were inspected twice by a single inspector. The R chart was based on the difference between the two repeat readings on each part. Twenty-five of the averages are beyond the control limits. All of the ranges are within the control limits. Comment on the repeatability of this measurement process and its suitability for use in SPC.*

    The repeatability of this measurement process is based on the R chart. Since the R chart is in control, the measurement process has consistent repeatability. The X-bar chart indicates that the measurement system can easily discriminate between units made by this process, thus it is suitable for SPC purposes. No mention is made here of the tolerance. However, if the process is used only for products where its capability is adequate the measurement system will have adequate repeatability.

(See section V.C Repeatability and reproducibility studies)

12. *Two inspectors each checked the same five parts twice. The average R value, based on repeat readings, is 2.5. All of the R values are within control limits. Compute the standard deviation for repeatability and the repeatability.*

$\sigma_e = 2.1552$, reproducibility = 11.0993.

(See section V.C Repeatability and reproducibility studies)

13. *In the above exercise the two inspectors' averages were 54.5 and 54.0. Find the reproducibility.*

1.45.

$$\frac{R_0}{d_2^*} = \frac{0.5}{1.41} = 0.3546$$

$$\text{Reproducibility} = \sqrt{\left(5.15\frac{R_0}{d_2^*}\right)^2 - \frac{(5.15\sigma_e)^2}{5 \times 2}}$$

$$= \sqrt{3.3352 - 1.2319} = 1.45$$

(See section V.C Repeatability and reproducibility studies)

B. DETAILED SOLUTIONS TO SELECTED PAST EXAM QUESTIONS

1. *How should measurement standards be controlled?*

    1. *Develop a listing of measurement standards with nomenclature and number for control.*

    2. *Determine calibration intervals and calibration sources for measurement standards.*

    3. *Maintain proper environmental conditions and traceability of accuracy to National Bureau of Standards.*

    a. 1 and 2 only

    b. 1 and 3 only

    c. 2 and 3 only

    d. 1, 2 and 3

    All three options are necessary for measurement standards control; choice *d* is correct. The CQE should be familiar with MIL-STD-45662; military standard requirements.

2. *When making measurements with test instruments, precision and accuracy mean:*

    a. the same.

    b. the opposite.

    c. consistency and correctness, respectively.

    d. exactness and traceability, respectively.

    e. none of the above.

    The terms "precision" and "accuracy" can be described using an analogy to target shooting with a rifle. If your shots are closely grouped, your shooting can be called *precise*, regardless of how far your grouping is from the bulls eye. If the bulls eye is at the center of the grouping your shooting is *accurate*, regardless of the scatter of the group. A close grouping centered at the bulls eye is both precise and accurate. Obviously precise and consistent are synonymous, as are accurate and correct; choice *c*. Note that there are much better definitions than those offered here, consult V.A in *The Complete Guide to the CQE*.

Precise but not accurate.

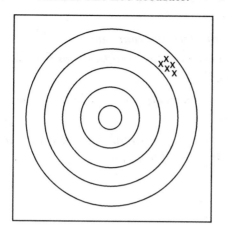

Accurate but not precise.

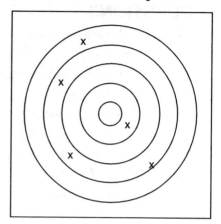

Accurate and precise.

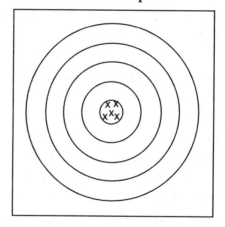

3. *A subsurface discontinuity in some purchased steel bar stock is a suspected cause for the high failure rate in your parts fabrication area. All of the following nondestructive test (NDT) methods could be used to screen the bar stock except:*

a. magnetic particle testing.

b. radiographic testing.

c. liquid penetrant testing.

d. eddy current testing.

e. ultrasonic testing.

Liquid penetrant inspection works by *penetrating*. This implies that the discontinuity must be exposed, which is not the case with a subsurface discontinuity. Choice *c* is correct.

(See chapter V.D Destructive and NDT testing concepts)

4. *One of the practical limits on the application of ultrasonic testing methods is:*

   a. lack of portability.

   b. poor penetration capability.

   c. reference standards are required.

   d. inability to record results permanently.

   Ultrasonic testing is extremely portable for an NDT method, with excellent penetration capabilities. Recorders exist that generate permanent inspection records (although these records are not as widely accepted as x-ray inspection film). One limitation of ultrasonic methods is the need to calibrate the equipment to detect a wide variety of flaws. Since different flaws produce different echo images and heights, it is difficult to produce reliable standards. Choice c is correct.

   (See chapter V.D Destructive and NDT testing concepts)

5. *Calibration intervals should be adjusted when:*

   a. no defective product is reported as acceptable due to measurement errors.

   b. few instruments are scrapped during calibration.

   c. the results of previous calibrations reflect few "out of tolerance" conditions during calibration.

   d. a particular characteristic on the gage is consistently found out of tolerance.

Of course, choice *d* describes a situation where the calibration interval should be shortened. The reader is again referred to MIL-STD-45662.
(See chapter V.B.3 Calibration systems)

6. *Holography is a non-destructive test technique which is used to:*
   a. measure hole locations with an optical device.
   b. measure the depth of "halos" around drilled holes using X-ray.
   c. measure the continuity of plated-through holes in printed wiring boards.
   d. measure surface displacements by recording interference patterns.
   e. measure flaws using acoustic vibration.

   Holography is a system of recording light or other waves on a photographic plate or other medium in such a way as to allow a three-dimensional reconstruction of the scene giving rise to the waves. The plate, or hologram, records the interference pattern between waves reflected by the scene and a direct reference wave at an angle to it. Choice *d* is the correct one.

C. ANSWERS TO SELECTED PAST EXAM QUESTIONS

1. *If not specifically required by the product drawing(s) or specification, non-destructive test (NDT) may be required during production and or during acceptance at the discretion of the quality engineer responsible for the inspection planning. This statement is:*
   a. false—because testing is limited to that specified by the design engineer.
   b. true—because NDT is a form of inspection (with enhanced senses) not a functional test.
   c. false—the QE may impose NDT as he believes necessary but cannot

delete it without design engineering permission.

d. true—because all acceptance testing and inspection requirements are up to quality engineering.

(*Answer: b.*)

2. A variable measurement of a dimension should include
   a. an estimate of the accuracy of the measurement process.
   b. a controlled measurement procedure.
   c. a numerical value for the parameter being measured.
   d. an estimate of the precision of the measurement process.
   e. all of the above.

(*Answer: e.*)

3. Calibration intervals should be adjusted when:
   a. no defective product is reported as being erroneously accepted as a result of measurement errors.
   b. few instruments are scrapped out during calibration.
   c. the results of previous calibrations reflect few out of tolerance conditions during calibration.
   d. a particular characteristic on a gage is consistently found out of tolerance.

(*Answer: d.*)

4. Accuracy is:
   a. getting consistent results repeatedly.
   b. reading to four decimals.
   c. using the best measuring device available.
   d. getting an unbiased true value.

(*Answer: d.*)

5. *Measurement error:*
   a. *is the fault of the inspector.*
   b. *can be determined.*
   c. *is usually of no consequence.*
   d. *can be eliminated by frequent calibrations of the measuring device.*
   (Answer: b.)

6. *Precision is:*
   a. *getting consistent results repeatedly.*
   b. *reading to four or more decimals.*
   c. *distinguishing small deviations from the standard value.*
   d. *extreme care in the analysis of data.*
   (Answer: a.)

7. *When specifying the "10:1 calibration principle" we are referring to what?*
   a. *the ratio of operators to inspectors.*
   b. *the ratio of quality engineers to metrology personnel.*
   c. *the ratio of main scale to vernier scale calibration.*
   d. *the ratio of calibration standard accuracy to calibrated instrument accuracy.*
   e. *none of the above.*
   (Answer: d.)

8. *Measuring and test equipment are calibrated to:*
   a. *comply with federal regulations.*
   b. *assure their precision.*
   c. *determine and/or assure their accuracy.*
   d. *check the validity of reference standards.*
   e. *accomplish all of the above.*
   (Answer: c.)

9. *A basic requirement of most gage calibration system specifications is:*
   a. all inspection equipment must be calibrated with master gage blocks.
   b. gages must be color coded for identification.
   c. equipment shall be labeled or coded to indicate date calibrated by whom, and date due for next calibration.
   d. gages must be identified with a tool number.
   e. all of the above.
   (Answer: c.)

10. *What four functions are necessary to have an acceptable calibration system covering measuring and test equipment in a written procedure?*
    a. calibration sources, calibration intervals, environmental conditions, and sensitivity required for use.
    b. calibration sources, calibration intervals, humidity control and utilization of published standards.
    c. calibration sources, calibration intervals, environmental conditions under which equipment is calibrated, controls for unsuitable equipment .
    d. list of standards, identification report, certificate number and recall records.
    e. all of the above.
    (Answer: c.)

11. *A qualification test is used to determine that design and selected production methods will yield a product that conforms to specification. An acceptance test is used to determine that a completed product conforms to design. On this basis, a destructive test can be used for:*
    a. qualification only.
    b. qualification or acceptance.
    c. acceptance only.
    d. neither qualification nor acceptance.
    (Answer: b.)

12. *Which of the following nondestructive testing methods is best for rapid inspection of l/2 in. diameter carbon steel rod one foot long for surface cracks?*
    a. radiography.
    b ultrasonic.
    c. magnetic particle.
    d liquid penetrant.
    (Answer: c.)

CHAPTER

VI

Safety and Reliability

A. SOLUTIONS TO SELECTED EXERCISES FOUND IN *THE COMPLETE GUIDE TO THE CQE*

1. *The mean time between failures a complex system is 5,000 hours. What is the failure rate?*

    0.0002 failures/hour.

    (See section VI.A Terms and definitions)

2. *A classic automobile has a MTBF of 6 months and a MTTR of 2 weeks. What is the availability?*

    92.31%

    (See section VI.A Terms and definitions)

3. *A computer system has an MTBF of 50,000 hours. It is purchased to be used as a network server, running 24 hours per day, seven days per week. What is the reliability of the system at t=30 days? t=365 days? If the MTTR is 16 hours, what is the availability of this system?*

    0.9857, 0.8393, 0.9997.

    (See section VI.A Terms and definitions)

4. *Review the data shown in Table VI.1 in* **The Complete Guide** *to the* **CQE.** *Assume that the drive mechanism consists of four elements in series: pulley, head, belt and capstan.*
   a. *If all four elements are apportioned equally, what must the reliability of each element be to reach the target reliability of 0.993 for the drive mechanism?*
   b. *Assume that the pulley, belt and capstan call all be built or bought with R=0.9995, what is the minimum reliability of the head?*
   c. *If the best available head has a reliability of 0.99, what must the combined reliability of the remaining three elements be to meet the goal of 0.993?*
   a. 0.9982
   b. 0.9945
   c. the target cannot be met since, for elements in series, the system cannot be more reliable than the least reliable element in the system.
   (See section VI.B Types of reliability systems)

5. *A string of three Christmas tree lights is arranged in series, i.e., if any light goes out the entire string fails to function. Sketch a reliability block diagram of this system. If R=0.99 for each individual light, what is the reliability of the entire string?*
   0.970299
   (See section VI.B.1 Series)

6. *A string of three Christmas tree lights is arranged in parallel, i.e., the entire string will fail to function only if all three lights go out. Failure is defined as all three lights failing to light. Sketch a reliability block diagram of this system. If R=0.95 for each individual light, what is the reliability of the entire string?*
   0.999875.
   (See section VI.B.2 Parallel)

7. *A string of six Christmas tree lights is arranged as follows: the first three lights are arranged in series and each light has a reliability of 0.99, the last three lights are arranged in parallel and each has a reliability of 0.95. Failure is defined as all six lights failing to light. Sketch a reliability block diagram of this system. What is the reliability of the entire string?*

    0.9701777.

(See section VI.B.2 Parallel)

8. *During busy periods, a volunteer fire department uses a standby dispatcher. The standby dispatcher's phone rings only if the full time dispatcher is handling a call. Sketch the reliability block diagram for this system.*

    See Figure VI.4 in *The Complete Guide to the CQE* as a guide.

(See section VI.B.3 Redundant)

9. *A Weibull distribution has been used to model reliability data for a complex system. The parameter ß is estimated to be 2.5. What phase of the product life cycle is indicated by this value of ß?*

    Wearout, since ß>1.

(See section VI.C Reliability life characteristics concepts)

10. *FMECA is usually performed during which phase of the product development cycle?*

    The reliability apportionment phase.

(See section VI.D Risk assessment tools)

11. *What is the fundamental problem with the use of "safety factors?"*

    Safety factors do not account for variation in either stress or strength.

(See section VI.D Risk assessment tools, page 508)

12. *A sample of power supplies from a stable process has been destructively tested to determine the voltage at which they burn out. The average burnout voltage was 136 and the standard deviation 5 volts. The line voltage in a typical installation averages 116 with a standard deviation of 3. Assuming normal distributions, compute the probability of failure, the reliability.*

    0.0003, .9997.

(See section VI.D Risk assessment tools)

B. DETAILED SOLUTIONS TO SELECTED PAST EXAM QUESTIONS

1. *When requesting "worst case" design analysis, you expect the Reliability Group to*

   a. analyze the worst rejects.

   b. analyze only those products failing to meet specification requirements.

   c. determine whether product requirements can be met with subassemblies assumed at their worst combination of tolerances.

   d. assume all subassembly tolerances at their maximum limit.

   Choice *c* describes worst case analysis. Worst case analysis is the traditional approach to tolerance evaluation. The modern approach also considers the *probabilities* associated with these "events" (e.g. an "event" is that two or more subassemblies are at their maximum tolerances).

2. *For a high compression aircraft air conditioning system, the MTBF is 100 hours. This mean life is allocated to four serial units comprising the total system. The unit failure rates are then weighted as follows:*

   $W_1 = 0.1250$
   $W_2 = 0.2500$
   $W_3 = 0.1875$
   $W_4 = 0.4375$

Based upon the above data, indicate which of the following is the correct calculation for one of

a. $\lambda_3 = 0.0018750$

b. $\lambda_4 = 0.0435700$

c. $\lambda_1 = 0.0125000$

d. $\lambda_3 = 0.0001875$

e. $\lambda_2 = 0.0025100$

A system with four serial units can be represented as follows:

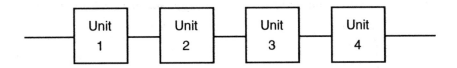

In such a system all four units must function or the system will fail. The reliability of this system can be easily determined as

$R_S = R_1 \times R_2 \times R_3 \times R_4$

where R_S = System reliability

          R_1 = Unit 1 reliability

          etc.

In words, the reliability of the system is the product of the unit reliabilities. If we can assume constant and independent failure rates, then

$$\lambda_s = \frac{1}{MTBF} = \frac{1}{\lambda_1 + \lambda_2 + \lambda_3 + \lambda_4}$$

where λ_S = the system failure rate

          λ_1 = unit 1 failure rate

    etc.

Relative unit weights are found using

$$W_j = \frac{\lambda_j}{\lambda_s}$$

Thus

$$\lambda_j = W_j \lambda_s \text{ or } \lambda_j = W_j/100$$

So

$$\lambda_1 = .00125; \qquad \lambda_2 = .00250$$
$$\lambda_3 = .001875; \qquad \lambda_4 = .004375$$

The only correct choice is choice *a*.

3. *What is the reliability of a system at 850 hours if the average usage on the system was 400 hours for 1650 items and the total number of failures was 145? Assume an exponential distribution.*

   a. 0%

   b. 36%

   c. 18%

   d. 83%

   Using the exponential

   $$R_S = e^{-t/MTBF}$$

   where

   R_S = System reliability at time t.

   t = Operating time

   MTBF = Mean time between failure

   e = 2.71828...

   The MTBF is

   $$MTBF = \frac{(Time)(Units)}{Failures} = \frac{(400)(1650)}{145} = 4552 \text{ hours}$$
   $$R_s = e^{-850/4552} = 83\%$$

   Choice *d*.

   (See section VI.A Terms and definitions)

4. **The probability of an accident for the head event "H" given below is**

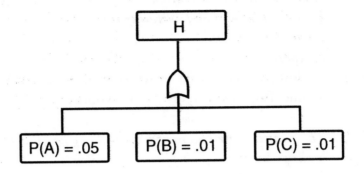

a. *.1125*

b. *.0689*

c. *.1100*

d. *None of the above.*

An accident will occur if event A *or* B *or* C recur. From probability theory we know that

$$P(A\cup B\cup C) = P(A) + P(B) + P(C) - P(A\cap B) - P(A\cap C) - P(B\cap C)$$
$$+ P(A\cap B\cap C)$$

So

$$P(H) = .05 + .01 + .01 - (.05)(.01) - (.05)(.01) - (.01)(.01)$$
$$+ (.05)(.01)(.01)$$
$$= .068905$$

Choice *b*.

(See section VI.D Risk assessment tools, & III.A.6 Basic probability concepts)

5. *A reliability data system usually implies collecting data on:*
   a. process machine downtime.
   b. product failures and operating time.
   c. maintenance costs.
   d. repair times.

   Most reliability data systems, such as GIDEP, collect data on product failures and operating times, choice *b*.

6. *The greatest contribution of a reliability effort is made in the:*
   a. design area.
   b. manufacturing area.
   c. shipping area.
   d. field service area.

   The contribution of the design function to product reliability is unquestionably the greatest; choice *a*.

7. *Preliminary hazard analysis:*
   a. is a review of safety problems prior to production.
   b. is normally done at a time when there is little design detail.
   c. can be used to identify the principal hazards when the product is first conceived.
   d. all of the above.

   Preliminary hazard analysis is a review of principal safety hazards performed when the product is first conceived. Choice *d* is correct.

8. *Inherent or intrinsic reliability:*
   a. is that reliability which can be improved only by design change.
   b. can be improved only by an improvement in the state of the art.
   c. is that reliability estimated over a stated period of time by a stated measurement technique.

d. is not an estimated reliability.

Inherent reliability is obtained by eliminating assignable causes of failure. Once this level is achieved failures occur at random and reliability can only be improved by design change, choice *a.*

9. *Reliability prediction is:*
   a. the process of estimating performance.
   b. the process of estimating the probability that a product will perform its intended function for a stated time.
   c. the process of telling "how you can get there from here."
   d. all of the above.

   Reliability is defined as the probability that a product will perform its intended function for a stated period of time. Reliability *prediction* is an attempt to estimate reliability, choice *b.*

10. *Basic sources of reliability data are:*
    1. In-plant testing.
    2. Field testing.
    3. Operation by user.
    a. 1 and 2
    b. 2 and 3
    c. 1 and 3
    d. 1, 2 and 3

    All of the selections are common sources of reliability data, choice *d.*

C. ANSWERS TO SELECTED PAST EXAM QUESTIONS

1. *Maintainability is:*

   a. the probability of a system being restored to functional operation within a given period of time.

   b. performing adequate maintenance on a system.

   c. probability of survival of a system for a given period of time.

   d. maintaining a machine in satisfactory working condition.

   e. none of the above.

   (Answer: a. See section VI.A Terms and definitions)

2. *In some reliability models redundancy may take the form of stand-by elements. What is the major disadvantage of such a model as regards its reliability?*

   a. more costly.

   b. reliability may be reduced by failure of sensing devices.

   c. failure rates are generally high.

   d. the system is too complex.

   e. none of these.

   (Answer: b. See section VI.B.3 Redundant)

3. *Product reliability is the probability of a product performing its intended function and under the operating conditions encountered. A significant element in this concept includes:*

   a. probability.

   b. performance.

   c. time.

   d. environment.

   e. all of the above.

   (Answer: e.)

4. *Parts in use during the "wearout" portion of the part life cycle curve will exhibit:*

   a. *a constant failure rate.*

   b. *a decreasing failure rate.*

   c. *a low failure rate.*

   d. *an increasing failure rate.*

   (Answer: d. See section VI.C Reliability life characteristic concepts)

5. *Reliability, maintainability, and product safety improvements are most often economically accomplished during the _____ phase of a program.*

   a. *design and development*

   b. *prototype test*

   c. *production*

   d. *field operation*

   e. *redesign and retrofit*

   (Answer: a. See section VI.D Risk assessment tools)

6. *Reliability testing of parts is performed to yield which of the following type of information?*

   a. *application suitability.*

   b. *environmental capability.*

   c. *measurement of life characteristics.*

   d. *all of the above.*

   e. *none of the above.*

   (Answer: d.)

7. *Failure mode, effect, and criticality analysis, (FMECA) is primarily for the purpose of:*
   a. *learning as much about the item as possible after qualification test.*
   b. *determining the way an item will most likely fail to help obtain design and procedural safeguards against such failures.*
   c. *determining, by extensive analysis, the reliability of an item.*
   d. *determining the cause of a failure, by dissecting the item, to help obtain corrective action.*
   (Answer: b. See section VI.D Risk assessment tools)

8. *According to the definition of reliability, performance over the expected or intended life is one criterion. In order to obtain a measurement for reliability, the actual life (t) must be compared to which of the following?*
   a. *sampling of components.*
   b. *Test cycles (T_C).*
   c. *Required life (T).*
   d. *MTBF.*
   e. *probability of failures (P_X).*
   (Answer: c. See section VI.A Terms and definitions)

9. *Maintainability of an equipment may be measured in terms of:*
   a. *maintenance dollar cost.*
   b. *maintenance man-hours.*
   c. *repair time.*
   d. *all of the above.*
   (Answer: d. See section VI.A Terms and definitions)

10. *The design function which assigns probability of failures between components or subsystems is called:*
    a. apportionment.
    b. significance.
    c. confidence
    d. qualification.
    (Answer: a. See section VI.B Types of reliability systems)

11. *A reliability test concluded during the pre-production stage is called:*
    a. demonstration test.
    b. acceptance test.
    c. significance test.
    d. qualification test.
    (Answer: d.)

12. *The concept of accelerated cycling or burn-in program of all devices for six months under normal operating conditions would:*
    a. reduce premature failures in use.
    b. improve constant failure rate probability.
    c. be of little use.
    d. assure an acceptable quality to the customer.
    (Answer: a. See section VI.C Reliability life characteristics concepts)

13. *In the failure rate model shown below, the part of the curve identified as A represents:*

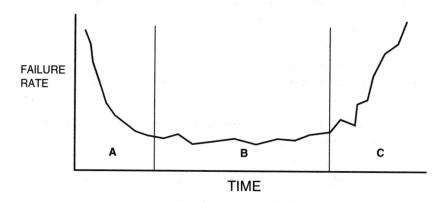

a. *the "bath tub" curve.*
b. *random and independent failures fitting a Poisson model.*
c. *the debugging period for complex equipment.*
d. *the wear-out period.*
(Answer: c. See section VI.C Reliability life characteristics concepts)

14. *The ratio:* $\dfrac{\text{probability density function (t)}}{\text{reliability (t)}}$ *is called:*

a. *useful life.*
b. *failure rate.*
c. *MTBF.*
d. *median.*
(Answer: b.)

15. *For the exponential model, the reliability at mean time to failure is about:*
a. *37%*
b. *50%*

c. 67%
d. 73%
(Answer: a. See section VI.B Types of reliability systems)

16.   *"Maintainability" is:*
      a. the probability that a system will not fail.
      b. the process by which a system is restored to operation after failure.
      c. a characteristic of design and installation.
      d. the time required to restore a system to operation after failure.
      (Answer: c. See section VI.A Terms and definitions)

17.   *Component 1 has an exponential failure rate of 3×10^4 failures per hour.*
      Component 2 normally is distributed with a mean of 600 hours and
      standard deviation of 200 hours. Assuming independence, calculate the
      reliability of the system after 200 hours.

      a. 0.878
      b. 0.918
      c. 0.940
      d. 0.977
      (Answer: b. See section VI.B.1 Series)

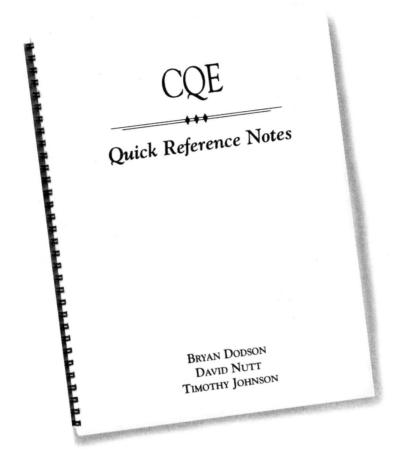